THE
LEGACY OF
CRYSTAL
ISLAND

BOOK ONE: THE AWAKENING

THE LEGACY OF CRYSTAL ISLAND

COLLEEN O'FLAHERTY-HILDER

Matador
9 Priory Business Park,
Wistow Road, Kibworth Beauchamp,
Leicestershire. LE8 0RX
Tel: 0116 279 2299
Email: books@troubador.co.uk
Web: www.troubador.co.uk/matador
Twitter: @matadorbooks

ISBN 978 1788035 163

British Library Cataloguing in Publication Data.
A catalogue record for this book is available from the British Library.

Printed and bound by CPI Group (UK) Ltd, Croydon, CR0 4YY
Typeset in 11pt Minion Pro by Troubador Publishing Ltd, Leicester, UK

Matador is an imprint of Troubador Publishing Ltd

To the bright star that is my daughter, Siobhan, whose presence in my life is a constant reminder of the magic that is Creation.

Contents

CHAPTER ONE

INNOCENCE

Orla walked into the flurry of activity that always accompanied the twins' bedtime routine, and observed the boundless energy and enthusiasm her children had for absolutely everything that appeared in their lives, an aspect of their personalities that never ceased to fill her with amazement and joy. Even the most repetitive of activities like bathing, cleaning teeth and putting on nightclothes triggered their mercurial imagination and enthusiasm in anticipation of what was to follow these mundane activities. But at the close of the day their excitability, whilst admirable, needed to be calmed so that Orla could continue with their bedtime ritual, the ritual that was preparing them for the unique and important role that would be their destiny. She clapped her hands with regal authority and lovingly ordered them into their respective beds, which they obeyed eagerly. As they climbed noisily into bed, and with the typical impatience of youth, they directed a stream of questions in stereo at Orla trying to guess, as if it were a game, what new aspect of their night time story would be revealed. Although the twins were only nine, their verbal reasoning was razor sharp and she normally loved the cut and thrust of their discussions but she had to silence them. Ignoring them completely, which was difficult, she picked up a dark green glass bottle from the bedside table and sprayed aromatic flower essences over their beds and around the room, delicately infusing the molecules of their bedroom with the memory of the plants, soothing and calming the frenetic activity of their young and fertile minds.

Sitting down in the easy chair between each of their beds she breathed deeply, lovingly placing her hands gently on each of their brows. When they eventually stopped speaking and closed their eyes, she began tracing the specific sequence of strokes on their foreheads that regulated their breathing until they were completely relaxed and receptive in the deepest parts of their memories, gently opening the doorway to the Crystaland promise of the Perfection of Eternity.

She sighed contentedly and took a moment to reflect over the time since the twins had been born. They were now nine years old and already beginning to demonstrate very different characteristics from those of previous royal children of Crystal Island. They were more enquiring, more intense in their pursuit of knowledge, and sometimes positively uncomfortable to be around, always pushing the boundaries and patience of their mentors. This personality progression had evolved because the prominent Crystaland genetic line had been duplicated and therefore intensified in twin children. In the history of Crystal Island this occurrence of royal twins was unique. In all the previous generations there had been only one child born to the Queen and her consort to ensure Crystal Wisdom was never diluted. When Orla had realised that she was bearing twins, she knew that this was heralding a new level of transformation for the Earth that would require an amplification of that Wisdom.

Whilst Orla was unsure of the detail of her children's future, she was relieved that the world they had been born into was a very different place from when she was young. Thanks to the efforts of Orla, her husband Finn and their team of helpers from Crystal Island, the Crystal memory had been reignited and completely awakened in the leaders of the world. This, thankfully, led to mankind being interrupted from its dystopian path of destruction and degeneration as they embraced and embodied all the gifts of Crystaland. The Earth had eventually healed, and a peaceful and abundant life had evolved for all. However, Orla knew that this was not the end of the story; there was much more to come. The royal family of Crystal Island would not be allowed to sit back and rest on its laurels. The transformation of Earth was just the beginning, and she knew her children were the key to that final challenge, the final piece in the jigsaw puzzle that would bring peace to all the worlds in all the universes.

Orla switched on the essential oil diffuser next to her chair and a stream of fragrant mist enveloped her as she breathed in deeply and rhythmically. With every breath the molecules of oils permeated her memory, penetrating and opening the many layers of Crystaland programming, allowing her to access a wealth of truth and knowledge. She settled deeper into the chair, fully relaxed in mind and body, and began the programming of her children's memories that had happened every night of their lives since they were babies. Their bedtime story was not from a book normally found on the book shelves of nurseries, it was the epic story of the gifting of Crystal Wisdom to the Earth, how mankind turned its back on Wisdom leading to a path of catastrophic near-destruction, and its final journey of transformation. Such was the intensely complex nature of the story, the children could not have fully comprehended the detail in their waking, conscious minds. Nor did they have the luxury of time afforded to her when she was young, to spend several years in the many worlds of Crystaland receiving the initiation into Crystal Wisdom. Her progeny had inherited intact, in every cell of their bodies, all of the Crystaland knowledge from both parents, but they also had to understand the disasters which befell the planet when the Crystaland laws of Wisdom were not followed. The Earth that the twins had inherited offered no evidence of that destructive aspect of history, so it was Orla's responsibility to instruct them, in a language and at a level that they could understand, what happened when the Crystaland laws were ignored.

When the twins were born, she had asked her mentors in Crystaland the best way to teach her children about Earth's dark history without them being overwhelmed, or indeed traumatised. They reminded Orla that, whilst having 80 per cent Crystal memory, the twins still retained human memory and suggested that she use the familiar time-honoured oral tradition of weaving complicated lessons about life into the safe tapestry of a fairy story.

So, each night she would start at the beginning, adding more and more of the detail as the days and years went by. The story gradually filtered through to their deep memory and influenced the development of their characters, the character necessary for the creation of brave pioneers who would one day push against the boundaries of their Elders to achieve the ultimate healing of the universe.

Orla brought her attention back to her children, focusing her mind in the unique way that she had of filtering through the levels of a person's deep memory, penetrating the layers of human experience and opening the chamber of their memory that was receptive to Crystal Wisdom, and she began the story... Princess Orla's story.

Once upon a time in the future there lay an enchanted island in the Atlantic Ocean, midway between what was later to become known as the east coast of America, and the south west coast of Ireland. It had once been part of the same continent but, after one of the many ice ages, the Earth had become warmer, the glaciers melted, the landmasses shifted and when the chaos had ceased, the parcel of land that was to be the island, had gently and quietly disengaged itself from all of its surrounding continents. At the moment of its freedom, the sea swept the little pocket of land into its secure embrace, holding it firmly from all other influences. This was a very special island unlike any body of land the Earth had seen before. It had grown out of turmoil and formed from a combination of the primal powers of centrifugal force, heat, and the indestructible continuum of Creation. A bejeweled island that was to be the place from whence the possibilities of all peace for the future generations of the planet hailed. Its name, Crystal Island.

After the ice age the Earth had been left dormant for thousands of years, covered in an impenetrable glacial sheet but, whilst there was stillness in its frozen outer world, the inner world was still warm and very much active; its fire having only been dimmed, not extinguished. Over the millennia, Earth's inner fire burned stronger, its fierce strength surging closer to the surface of the sea bed and, when all the elements were in perfect alignment, the fire burst violently into the icy waters of the ocean releasing a multitude of atoms from the Earth's core urgently seeking their rightful place in the next chapter of Earth's story of necessary transformation and evolution.

To ensure the success of this particular cycle of transformation, all the knowledge of Creation had to be released and dispersed around the planet to activate Earth's, beautiful and natural gifts. The vehicle to transmit this information was the Earth's minerals; the basic building blocks of all life on Earth that had not changed or been distorted over the millennia, remaining in their original form since the beginning of eternity. Each mineral held within its atomic structure the pure memory of all Creation and each mineral carried its own unique intelligence knowing exactly what its role was in the multifarious options of Creation. But, as is so often the case, this process was not so straightforward. This latest explosion of the seabed had been so ferocious that it had catapulted the atoms chaotically into the ocean and the key minerals, being the most reactive, had become disassociated from their core groups causing confusion and conflict. A situation that was far from conducive for transformation. For the successful broadcasting of Creation's knowledge, the minerals had to be in their correct form and synergy to activate their collective intelligence that carried the original imprints of Creation.

With a keen sense of urgency, their survival memory scoured the waters searching for that unique pulsing rhythm of the energy that would help them to regroup and, at that precise catalytic moment, when all the minerals connected in their correct groupings, the doorway of Crystal Wisdom would fly open allowing Earth's natural gifts to be birthed.

Throughout its physical experience, Earth had undergone many cycles of eruption, cooling, transformation, transfiguration and evolution which had ultimately been a protracted process of purification; that which was found to be redundant or harmful for a particular stage of the planet's evolution did not survive. The particular location of the island in the ocean had gone through a much more intense and rapid process, which had resulted in this small landmass becoming a reflection of the pure essence of all of Earth's natural gifts; all the magnificence of Creation had been brought together in this one small but noble island. And the sea had recognised in this island those unique qualities and had lovingly surrendered daily doses of Wisdom onto its shores; every wave whispering the memory of eternity into the atoms of the crystalline sand, forming and shaping the future of its landscape and ultimately the future of the planet.

The Wisdom increased the intensity of the atoms' magnetic strength that pulsed sound waves through the Earth's waters and they became powerful beacons for information that was felt by other atoms thousands of miles away stretching into every corner and distant recess of the planet. They responded collectively to that primal call, the signature melody of the universe, gathering and speedily navigating towards the deep pulsating rhythm that rippled through the waters of the vast oceans. The object of their intense attraction was this unique island that had taken all the memory from the larger landmasses, condensed it into a much smaller body of land and, combined with the intelligence of the ocean, had produced an amplification of magnetic strength far greater than anywhere else on the Earth; broadcasting a sound like no other that had been heard in the planet's very long and troubled history.

As the tiny atoms journeyed eagerly through the oceans towards the island, they combined and connected into larger and larger groups. Their collective intelligence recognised and identified the rich qualities of this island, which they knew needed to be preserved and protected at all cost. They understood that the planet could not continue with the constant depleting cycles of destruction, which had caused so many shifts in its structure; the next process of transformation had to be completely successful – there could be no mistakes this time.

Eventually and predictably, over a relatively short period, the atoms made their way towards the perimeter of the island, collected and regrouped themselves into 1144 large diamond shaped crystalline pillars, implanting themselves deeply and securely into the seabed forming a protective circle. Each crystal pillar reflected a different colour from the multilayered hues of the aqua of the sea, the blues of the sky and the many shades of brightness from the sun's rays. Once in place the crystal pillars not only protected the island, they were also a constant source of stabilisation to all the minerals of the oceans, assisting in the regrouping of those atoms that had become lost and disenfranchised in the original explosion of chaos that inhibited and suppressed their individual intelligence. The creation of the Crystal Fortress was complete, and Crystal Island was born.

In those early days when the sun shone on the Crystal Fortress, shards of light bounced back and forth from each crystal pillar, each one reflecting the brilliance of the other, and that reflection bounced off the surface of the sea creating a crisscross of light and a melody of subtle sounds which formed a dome of musical brilliance radiating for many miles like a gigantic jewel, glittering and singing happily on its own adorning the vast openness of the ocean.

It was some time after this, that supra intelligent travellers from a far off galaxy were attracted to planet Earth. These travellers were a species who had first been alerted by the sound radiating from Earth's solar system. Their attention intensified when they identified the melodic activity of planet Earth. As they entered Earth's solar system and travelled closer to the planet, they recognised that the frequency of sound was similar to that of their own planet – only Earth's tune was discordant – they were immediately intrigued.

These beings were not like the majority of travellers found in this cosmos, and indeed there were many, they were not only supra intelligent but their physical appearance was very different. Their structure was crystal-like, but with a much higher energy value than that of Earth's crystal, to the point that they were not material; they had form but were not dense; they needed neither food or water; nor did they need to use words to communicate with each other. These were the Crystalanders, the Guardians of Eternal Wisdom. Their sole responsibility being to surf the open vastness of space seeking galaxies, solar systems and planets that had fallen out of balance with Creation's rhythm and, for the continuum of Creation, it was critical that this rhythm was never interrupted for very long.

However, other travellers of the cosmos who had very different agendas and much lower intelligence, nearly always created the greatest imbalance. The whole of outer space was full of explorers from different universes and galaxies with varying levels of intelligence, who sometimes brought with them very different intentions; they plundered and took what they wanted from each solar system leaving behind shells of former planets. Those species were often the product of a planet in the process of transformation and evolution that had tired of the discipline and responsibility required to adhere to the Wisdom of Creation, and had decided to make their own rules, which was always a disaster. So they took what they thought was the easiest and quickest route for survival – take and consume rather than nurture and conserve. In response to this abuse, the planet would rebel, take action and withdraw into itself rendering its environment uninhabitable.

When the Crystalanders arrived on Earth they were immediately impressed by what they saw; a planet made of crystal. Not the crystal from which they came, but a simpler form of crystal constructed from minerals with a less sophisticated structure. The Earth was covered in different forms of crystal, from the gigantic pieces of crystal rock, which appeared randomly on the landscape, down to the beautiful red crystalline soil that covered the vast open planes of the planet. The waterways were liquid crystal as the same minerals present in the soil were present in the water. The Crystalanders saw that these minerals were quite primitive, but that there was potential for further transformation; new minerals from their galaxy could be added to the mix enabling transformation and evolution to take place. The basic ingredients for Crystaland intelligent life were present in the atoms of minerals and that was all that would be required to begin the process.

However, unfortunately, the Crystalanders were not working with a completely blank canvas. Previously, the Earth had been visited by rogue galactic explorers who had left their mark of disrespect behind them. The rich supply of high quality minerals on Earth was the attraction, but they had needed a workforce for the extraction of minerals from the Earth's crust. So, in a quest to provide a constant supply of strong workers with limited mental faculties, they had begun to experiment with life, and the results of these experiments were the primitive humanoids that the Crystalanders found inhabiting Earth – desperate creatures with primitive brains trying to survive in an unforgiving and terrifying terrain, their coarse behaviour being mirrored in their appearance. But, the Crystalanders identified that, underneath the aggressive behaviour, they could see that these poor beings were frightened and lost, and they desperately needed help. Their days were a constant battle for survival; they had no natural Wisdom so were confused and confounded by nature. Fear stalked their waking hours and nightmares plagued their dreams. The Crystalanders realised that these beings had been manufactured as an experiment solely to create a beast of burden requiring great strength but minimal intelligence and, whilst they were like this, it was impossible for them to become Crystal Guardians of planet Earth. They had been developed before the last ice age when Earth's minerals were being plundered and, as soon as the mineral stores were depleted, the travellers had abandoned Earth seeking another planet, which offered an abundance of natural wealth, to be pillaged. They had left behind the humanoids, discarding them without a second glance. When the ice age had eventually taken a grip on Earth, their numbers had gradually diminished. The freezing temperatures of that ice age had reduced their numbers considerably, so that only the very strongest had survived but, without their creators, they had no way of knowing how to use their physical strength constructively. They were like children inhabiting physically strong bodies with powerful primitive hormones coursing through their veins, affecting their thought patterns and behaviour, driving them relentlessly through cycles of fear and aggression.

As part of the same experiment, those travellers had introduced animals to the planet, which were grotesque – huge, ferocious and highly predatory. These animals had failed in their ability to serve the travellers so they were used as a food supply for man and were contained in secure pens for this purpose. There was no possibility of these animals being a reflection of the beauty of Creation; it was as if their creators were in a genetic laboratory in the deepest and darkest corner of the cosmos. When the travellers left, the animals eventually escaped from their prisons and roamed the continents looking for food and revenge. Those poor Earthlings were desperate creatures who had very few natural skills with which to defend themselves against their predators or the harshness of their environment. There was no respite from fear and with no other terms of reference, they had eventually begun to reflect the behaviour of those predatory animals that constantly stalked the perimeter of their lives.

The Crystalanders looked down on Earth and felt great sadness. Here was a beautiful planet that echoed so many facets of Crystaland, but it needed Crystal Wisdom to allow it to develop onto its next stage of transformation. If the planet continued without help, then the crystalline structures would disintegrate and they knew very well what the results would be, they had seen it many times over the aeons, the destruction of yet another planet affecting the balance of its solar system, which then in turn disrupted the harmony of the cosmos. When this happened the Crystalanders would have to charge into every corner of the many universes trying to maintain order and synergy so that balance could once again be restored.

Increasingly, the only way that they could maintain balance was by leaving planets as wastelands: basically putting the planets into a dormant phase. Every aspect of life had to be extinguished. This was a radical step but it allowed the vibration of the planet to stabilise and allow the wizardry of nature to begin the rebuilding process. Once a planet was in dormant phase it stopped attracting interest from negative visitors who would be hell-bent on plundering its vitality, no matter how small. However, the reality was that more and more planets were being put into dormancy, which eventually would downgrade the energy of the whole cosmos. The universe to which Earth belonged was in this category. If the Crystalanders couldn't find a solar system to reboot its universe, then that particular universe would die. They knew that this could be a real eventuality, it had happened many times before and, when it did happen, they would have no choice. With great reluctance, they would abandon the cause, travel to another universe in a different dimension to continue Creation's work, leaving Earth's solar system to drift further and further into the darkest depths of infinity.

The dimension of the Crystaland universe was a glittering collection of stunningly beautiful galaxies, suns, stars and planets, completely impenetrable from dark forces, each and every one of its particles of existence reflecting the perfection and beauty of Creation. This was the universe from where all the knowledge of Creation came – The Home of the Eternal Wisdom of Creation.

The universe to which Earth's solar system belonged had once been a satellite of Crystaland but, like many other satellites, it had become disconnected and downgraded over its many cycles of evolution. Unfortunately, with separation from the Eternal Wisdom, came accelerated degeneration that eventually prevented healing and transformation. Without the constant transformative development required to keep pace with Creative Wisdom, solar systems would slip deeper and deeper into the abyss of fear and darkness.

And so, satisfied with the condition of Earth's crystals, the Crystalanders looked for the perfect place to start their experiment. They knew that they had enough of the raw ingredients to translate the Gifts of Wisdom from Crystaland to Earth but they had to find the best representation of life to begin the process of reprogramming. Their critical gaze eagerly fell onto the island with its unique crystal formation. They could see that the Crystal Fortress formed a protective dome and they knew there was a very good reason for this; crystals were attracted to Wisdom in its purest form and therefore the degenerative process would be minimised.

When the Crystalanders scanned the island they discovered that the inhabitants were unlike the humans that they had encountered in other landmasses on Earth; their appearance was less coarse and their manner softer.

13

The islanders appeared more refined because of two major reasons: the animals on the island were far less predatory therefore reducing fear; and the energy level of the island itself was more powerful than the rest of the planet because of the concentration and formation of its crystals coupled, of course, with its powerful Crystal Fortress. Unlike the rest of Earth, crystals on the island were a collection and reflection of all the colours of Creation and appeared all over the island in compressed groups of coloured light. The rain fell down through the crystalline structures and carried their atomic Wisdom into the waterways of the island providing a source of energetic nourishment for the minds and bodies of its population. These humans had smaller skulls than other humanoids, but the structure of their brain allowed for reprogramming of memory, which was necessary for them to receive the complexity of Crystaland knowledge. Physiologically the inhabitants were also different from other humans, as they had evolved from only two main tribes. Before the ice age, the Americas and Europe had been one landmass populated with humans of many and various physiological differences, the result of the genetic engineering of their creators. But, when the island broke away from the other continents, its population was fed from just two main tribal groups one was small, dark skinned, with jet black hair and the other tall, blond and fair.

Whilst the Crystalanders knew that the Crystal Fortress gave sufficient protection from outside negative influences, providing the necessary isolation for the experiment to take place totally undisturbed, they had to ensure that the rest of the planet was suitable for its eventual transformation. So they made several reconnaissance expeditions to Earth over a period of time to assess how it was developing before making the final decision to colonise.

On the Earth at that time, there were formations of large white crystal pillars dotted around the planet in various terrains but they were quite chaotically arranged and it was the emission of their chaotic sound that attracted rogue cosmic travellers. Whenever the Crystalanders travelled to planets that contained crystals, the first thing they did was to take the indigenous crystals and put them into unique geometric shapes on the planet's natural magnetic energy points to balance and help with its correct evolution.

Once organised in their correct formation, these Earth crystals also provided the energy requirements that humans needed for their comfortable survival. As the humanoids were made of very dense material and possessed only primitive intelligence, the need for an efficient energy source was a priority before the experiment could begin. The Earth cooled at different times of its day and different cycles of time depending on which landmass was exposed to its sun. It was imperative that Earthlings had a form of energy that could provide both heat and light when their sun was obscured. Equally, as their bodies began to transform and they became less coarse and primitive, they would require more heat and protection. Their original creators had shown humans how to cut down trees and use the wood as fire for this purpose. Trees grew in great forests all over the planet providing the necessary air balance for the humans but more importantly, the trees provided sacred knowledge, which diminished with the felling of each tree. The Crystalanders knew that as the population increased there would be increasing requirements for energy so they created a special configuration of crystals that would provide heat, light and energy depending on its geometric formation.

And so, when the Crystalanders were confident that all the ingredients necessary were in place, the great experiment began. When all the physical qualities of the island had been conducive, the Crystalanders had eventually integrated their genetic memory with those of the people of the island and this programming had continued to reinforce the Crystal Gifts with every generation, guaranteeing Crystal Wisdom would be unchallenged. This was Earth's last chance to reverse its many cycles of destruction.

In the 22nd century, Crystal Island was still functioning, for the most part, according to the original teachings of the Crystalanders who had arrived on its shores hundreds of thousands of years before. At that time, the island had many natural resources with an abundance of plants unusually enriched with nutrients benefitting from its position in the ocean providing a subtropical climate. It was truly like paradise with everyday living following the rules of Crystal Wisdom.

The protective Crystal Fortress surrounding the island had been calibrated by the Crystalanders to enhance its energy ensuring that no foreign vessel – air or seaborne – could come into its waters or air space; even the latest sophisticated navigational tools couldn't find it, nor could they come upon it by accident. As soon as the crystal boundary detected vessels, it emitted a sound wave that scrambled their radar and pushed them onto a different course. It was only by invitation that anyone could penetrate the protective barrier but, although it was possible to create a pathway for foreign vessels to enter the island's waters, strangers in the 22nd century were unable to set foot on the island. Its vibration was now so different from the rest of the world that those few people who had visited quickly became ill and their nervous systems had become overloaded causing irreparable harm to both their bodies and minds.

Whilst the island still enjoyed a magical life, this was

not the case for the rest of the world; a creeping negativity had eventually begun to make a reappearance in mankind which had instigated a spiral of degeneration that would eventually have terrible consequences for the planet. The surface of the Crystal Fortress had begun to degenerate slightly because of the world's pollution, but it still held its crystal form: the surface had changed to a rock-like substance, but underneath the crystal still emitted an energy field of sound that was impenetrable by man's relatively simple technology. Communication with the rest of the world, both digitally and energetically, were excellent and the people of Crystal Island looked on in despair and confusion as they watched the world begin to turn in on itself.

The Queen of Crystal Island, whilst being human, had direct lineage to the first of the original supra beings from Crystaland who had come to Earth. The female child inherited the royal line and the Queens' consorts came from the same ancient lineage so that the Crystal Wisdom was never diluted or lost. At this time in the 22nd century, the Queen of Crystal Island, Maeve, and her consort Patrick, had a beautiful daughter, Princess Orla. The royal families only ever had one child, which guaranteed the integrity of their genetic memory. Had there been more than one child, the memory could have been diluted. Unlike everywhere else on the planet there was no fear that one child might not reach maturity for this island retained all the original Crystal knowledge of healing and regeneration that had been practised and perfected over thousands and thousands of years.

All the initiated female adult members of the royal family were able to travel with their inner sight across the planet and see in much more detail the gravity of what was really happening. At that time all forms of public information was controlled by the world governments who were painting a picture that was far from the truth; the general public always being given a sanitised version. Spin-doctors had become so adept at bending the truth out of shape that the boundaries between the truth and illusion were very blurred. But, if the horrendous truth had been revealed, there would have been anarchy, revolution and therefore chaos. Human history had demonstrated that the results of revolution, which was usually initiated out of a sense of outrage at the imbalance of power, generally meant that change regressed into the same behaviour as before, only dressed in a different cloak. When the new leaders took over the reins of power their only terms of reference in their memories were the policies of previous leaders so nothing really changed. Crystal Wisdom, the precious gift from the Crystalanders, which would have given them creative solutions to their problems, had receded centuries before into the darkest recesses of their memories.

In the past the royal family of Crystal Island had made overtures to leaders of other countries in an effort to persuade them to live a more natural life, but they didn't want to listen, believing that the island was a quirk of nature. But the food supply of these countries was running out and they desperately sought a food product that had concentrated nutrients to feed the starving masses. Ironically, whilst there was a shortage of food, the birth rate was increasing. The constant supply of babies was a sign that the planet was desperately trying to prevent this species from completely destroying itself. Unfortunately, many babies born out of starvation rarely reached adulthood as they were sentenced to a short life filled with hunger and disease. Earth's Wisdom recognised that these desperate people still had a quality deep within their memory which could help reverse the planet's degeneration and annihilation. Creation therefore conspired to increase the fertility in the weak and frail in the hope that mankind could at least hang on by its fingertips to the precipice of the travesty of life that it had become. Crystal Island had a unique plant product that had once grown abundantly in all the fields of the world but the pollution created by man had destroyed it elsewhere decades ago. The feeding generals of the Federation of Countries pleaded for seeds and specimens from the island to try to grow the plant in special conditions but it was hopeless; the soil of the planet had degenerated and the air was so polluted that it shrivelled the new shoots as soon as they struggled to break through the depleted soil.

The royal male line of Crystal Island came from an especially strong crystal-human genetic line that had the responsibility for communicating and interfacing with these Earth leaders. Whilst there was total equality between the sexes on the island, the rest of the world had begun to turn its back on any authority of women. Equally, the female royal line functioned at a very high level of Crystal Wisdom, which needed to be protected from the harshness and ugliness of the methods of communication of Earth's leaders. Orla's father, Patrick, had given repeated warnings of the dangers of Earth's farming systems, advising the agricultural scientists to change the way they treated their fields so that the soil could repair and once again be bountiful. But they didn't understand and, what was more heartbreaking, they didn't want to listen. These high-octane leaders were responsible for creating a monster out of the planet and Earth was slowly and thoroughly devouring itself. These same leaders persisted in trying to find answers to their multi-dimensional complex problems that confounded them on a daily basis, which were actually created by their one-dimensional science. The flaw was that they were looking for complex answers from a restricted form of science, which was blind to the complete picture of life. The results were disastrous; they would make a development in one area, which in turn, caused depletion in another. The royal family of Crystal Island judged this as a form of insanity; from their perspective, all vestiges of any form of intelligence had been put aside and replaced with madness. The scientists of Earth overlooked one vital fact which was that nature's intelligence can never be replicated in a test tube efficiently: there is more to the balanced functioning of a living planet than that which can be identified by man's limited science.

The Queen, whose legacy gave her direct contact with Crystaland, had been told by her Crystal mentors that one day the Earth would become so desperate that there would be a revolution of thought. She knew that there was an alliance of people on the planet who had tried to live life differently by embracing Crystaland teachings, but they were derided and seen as eccentric by the decision makers of the world. But the Queen knew that, come the time when nature turned its back on science completely, when the scientists could give no more answers and the world was spinning on its axis into a pit of destruction, it would take such a small group of people to start a new community for planetary healing.

With this in mind, she was conscious that her daughter was coming to an age of initiation when she would start to be assimilated into the ancient Crystaland knowledge, ensuring her understanding of the Crystal Wisdom and, more importantly, learn what would happen if that Wisdom was not followed. Maeve knew that the continuation of this knowledge in its original form was the most important legacy ever to be handed down to future generations. At that moment in time Orla lived a charmed life in this paradise haven of Crystal Island and was blissfully unaware of what the outside world truly looked like and, more importantly, what would happen if the Crystaland legacy were to die.

It was a knowledge that went beyond reason and logic and went beyond the three-dimensional human world. It was a knowledge that had to be experienced in the deepest part of their memory in order to transform all vestiges of the human fear memories, which had been so deeply implanted in those early primitive years of mankind's history. The language of fear and the language of Crystal Wisdom were incompatible. Each level of fear in a person's memory had to be rewritten in the language of Crystal Wisdom for the complete revelation of Wisdom to occur.

Crystal Island had offered to give a version of this knowledge to the world's Federations in a form thought to be at a level that the ordinary man could understand and assimilate, but this would have taken time and, unfortunately, the leaders had no patience. They wanted to fast track people, cut corners and get results quickly. It was an impossible task because their science was still very primitive in its understanding of how the human mind functioned. In addition, the many wonderful facets of the crystal-human mind had become dulled over time owing to the destructive effects of fear on the chemistry of the human brain. Added to that cocktail was the damaging effect of the ever present polluted environment and the number of chemical medications over zealously administered to balance the minds of people whose emotional functioning fell outside of their restrictive parameters of normal. Earth had definitely become the planet of the 'quick fix' kings. But, short cuts never work well with Creation; an oak tree doesn't evolve from an acorn to a full-grown tree, in all its wonderful glory, in one giant step. In Crystal Wisdom, there is a plotted path of transformational development and, if any of the steps of this path are skipped, then chaos unfolds.

And so, on Orla's 14th birthday Queen Maeve told her that she was of an age to start her initiation into Crystal Wisdom and her grandmother, Grace, would accompany her for part of the journey. Her grandmother had once been a beautiful vibrant queen but as she had become older, and Orla had no idea how old she was, she had needed more rest and had eventually happily handed over the title with its incumbent responsibilities to her daughter Maeve, as was the custom. All three women bore a strong resemblance but their colouring differed. They were petite in body and all had thick straight long hair, the fairest of skin, beautiful almond shaped eyes that were framed with luxuriant black lashes. As the females of the royal family increased their Crystal initiation, their hair and eyes began to change colour. Orla had black/brown hair and deep hazel eyes with flecks of green, fully reflective of the Earth's rich tones, Maeve had sprinklings of white hair interlacing her beautiful thick dark hair and her eyes were pale jade green. Grace's hair had turned completely white and fell thickly in silky braids around her shoulders but her eyes held the most remarkable of these changes. They had become lightened to a piercing silver grey and Orla would often spend moments staring into her grandmother's eyes drawn to their depth and clarity; it was as if her eyes were portals to many worlds which held the promise of eternity. Orla was bursting with the excitement and enthusiasm of a young girl brought up to embrace knowledge, change and challenge. She had not a shred of apprehension only excitement. She had heard about the initiation, of course, her whole life but had no conception of what it would be like but she sensed that it would be magical.

Before Orla could go on her journey of initiation Maeve and Grace knew that she needed to be formally bound to her future consort. The binding ceremony was important as it entwined the emotional memory of the two individuals enabling the consort to experience the initiations that Orla would be receiving, but in a more subtle way. The royal male line underwent their own initiation into Crystal Wisdom to fully understand their personal responsibilities. Orla had grown up with a group of young boys from the royal families and had increasingly become attached to Finn. Prince Finn was also 14, very tall with coarse red curly hair, and the deepest blue eyes. Although he had by no means developed physically, there was already promise in his young body of that phenomenal super strength that his genetic line manifested as they developed into manhood. As yet Orla had no comprehension of the qualities of the different Crystaland worlds that she would experience during her initiation, but there was one in particular that was the home of strength and power where Finn would need to spend several years before they could be together as husband and wife.

During their free time they were inseparable, spending their days enjoying each other's company, talking and laughing, or riding their horses wildly across the beautiful fields and forests of the island. Grace had been told of their union by her Crystal mentors when Orla and Finn were babies, but the adults of the royal line knew that nothing could be forced, their relationship had to evolve naturally.

Maeve and Patrick had observed the closeness of the two developing over the years and happily approached Orla asking if she would like to be promised to Finn. She squealed with delight. She was as yet unaware of the complexities of adult relationships, but knew that on a very deep level she and Finn were one, and she adored him. Finn's parents had asked him the same question and he was equally delighted; he had felt exactly the same as Orla, he loved her spirit, her enthusiasm for life and was captivated in his own innocent way by her promise of beauty.

The binding ceremony took place in the sacred circle of crystals, which had been created when the Crystalanders first came to the island for such occasions as this. Grace led the small party, Orla and Finn accompanied by the two sets of parents. Grace was responsible for administering all of the seven sacred Earth initiations for the royal family, which protected and preserved the Crystaland memory. Orla looked at Finn carefully taking in every detail of his face. She knew that she would be away for several years and she wanted to remember him accurately. He was much taller than she, with a strong jawline showing just the suggestion of a red beard and Orla knew that when she saw him again he would have developed into a strong man, both physically and mentally. Grace took the two young people into the centre of the crystal circle and sat them on a large white crystal seat just large enough for two people. She bound their hands together with golden crystal ribbon and then took a small container of oils extracted from the roots of plants, which released a vapour-like substance around the heads of the two young people, relaxing them and opening their minds for the next stage. Grace placed her left hand on Orla's head and her right hand on Finn's. They closed their eyes and Grace began to sing a song that had been given to the royal family by the Crystalanders for the binding ceremony. It was a song from another dimension and could be discerned only by the members of the royal family. To the uninitiated it looked as if she was in a trance. Grace sang the song of binding which activated the memory in the circle of crystals surrounding them. As the song progressed the ancient carvings on the crystals became illuminated and the light that each one produced gathered into a swirling pool and hovered over the heads of the young couple. This opened the deeper recesses of memory in Orla and Finn's minds so that they could access and assimilate the memory stored in the crystals and, using the skill that had been taught to Grace by her Crystal mentors, she focused her creative mind into theirs and irreversibly merged the memories of Orla and Finn. Initially the two young people felt giddy, then they experienced a feeling of mind expansion, which took them to a point of extreme bliss. When Grace finished the song the swirling light disengaged itself from the couple and gradually retreated back into the crystals. The two young acolytes eventually opened their eyes and looked at each other, and there it was, they were looking into the other's heart and knew every twist and turn of their emotions. The binding was complete and although Orla and Finn had to leave the island to complete their initiations, they would always be connected to each other emotionally so their physical separation would be almost meaningless.

The following morning Orla's journey began. Grace and Orla made their farewells and set out on one of the many sunny mornings on Crystal Island to the famous Secret Garden. The day was magical: the sun was shining, the sky was blue without a cloud in the sky and a cool breeze brushed Orla's cheeks as she walked through the lush countryside. Only members of the royal family and twelve specialist gardeners were ever allowed access to the garden. As they neared the walled garden, Grace stopped at a huge oak door, which was thick, solid, heavy and kept in pristine condition. She retrieved a key from her jacket pocket, unlocked the door and pushed it open with amazing ease. Orla was intrigued at her grandmother's strength as the door looked as if ten men would be needed to push it open. As she walked into the entrance of the garden, she observed the gardeners, who were male and had been chosen from a family with the honour of holding this responsibility for thousands of years. On Crystal Island responsibilities that involved the perpetuation of the Crystal Wisdom were handed down from generation to generation to ensure that not one tiny shred of knowledge was lost.

Orla began walking into the garden and then stood still in amazement, her eyes were like orbs as she quickly took in the breathtaking beauty of her surroundings. The normal gardens of Crystal Island were gorgeous, but this garden was a hundred times more abundant, bursting at the seams with colour and fragrance. It was therefore no surprise that in this garden of paradise special plants were grown for the rejuvenation of the body and the expansion of the mind. As Orla and Grace made their way through the garden, Orla's attention was drawn to the intensity of each gardener's focus whilst undertaking his duties. They were all strong men with capable, sturdy bodies but, on closer inspection, she noticed that they had the gentlest of hands. They treated every plant as if they were precious living beings, gently and skillfully caressing newly budding plants, and when it was necessary to take its buds or blooms to make remedies, they would talk to the plant in a language Orla was yet to understand. In this garden, the soil was still crystalline; it had kept its structure all these years as the intention of its gardeners was pure and they nurtured the plant life with love. The garden in turn reflected that love back in the beauty that erupted from its soil on a daily basis.

All the trees in the garden were tall, strong and ancient. As Orla scanned the garden, taking in every little detail in wonder, joy, and amazement, she noticed that there was a grove of trees that looked like a collection of wise old men scrutinising the day-to-day activities of the garden. Her grandmother led her to the grove and explained to her that these seven trees were the Guardians of the Secrets of Evolution and therefore held the knowledge of all life, each tree embodying a specific quality of Wisdom. The trees had taught the gardeners how to choose the buds from selected trees to make remedies so that mankind could imbibe the qualities of each tree. Each tree was making an offering to mankind which reunited them with the perfection of nature and reminded them of the qualities required that were important for the evolution of any community.

Grace introduced Orla to each tree and explained their individual qualities to her. The oldest and tallest tree whose old branches grew out and then down towards the ground, donated Loyalty and Incorruptibility; the second tree had the deepest roots and donated Faithfulness and Friendship; the third was smaller, producing pine cones, it gave Vigilance; the fourth was a smaller tree still, producing dark berries which gave Protection through purification of thoughts; the fifth tree was tall with the widest trunk Orla had ever seen and gave Intuition; the sixth tree had the widest branches acting like a huge canopy over the green carpet-like grass of the garden and this tree gave the understanding of Duty; the final tree had thick dark green prickly leaves and this tree gave the most important quality for transformation, Courage.

If the gardeners needed guidance on the design of the garden, it was the trees that communicated the correct information, which ensured the continuity, synergy and rhythm of the garden at all times. There was a symbiosis between the plant life and the gardeners that was truly both captivating and confusing. Grace, seeing the puzzled look on the young girl's face, reminded her that all would be revealed during her journey of initiation. Orla totally accepted this and was immediately distracted by the intoxicating fragrances pouring from the heavily scented flowerbeds. She quickly identified the familiar fragrances of the different plants: lavender, rose, geranium, rosemary, ylang-ylang and so it continued until her mind began to gently relax and unfold, preparing for the knowledge that she would be receiving on her journey.

As they progressed further into the centre of the garden, they came upon the oldest tree Orla had ever seen. She recognised it as being one of the grove of trees. Grace explained that this type of tree was the first ever to have appeared on earth, dating back 200 million years and carried the entire memory of the planet. This particular tree was nearly 4000 years old and its extremely thick trunk was covered in a thick protective layer of ivy. Grace moved close to the tree and spoke softly in a language that once again Orla could not identify. With a smile of gratitude, Grace gently moved aside the long tentacles of ivy revealing an opening large enough for them to walk through. Grace walked into the opening, followed closely by the slightly bemused Orla, which led them to a spherical crystalline vessel, gleaming from its own internal light. This vessel had been in the tree since the beginning of their people's memory and it had not deteriorated one iota. It was crafted from a substance that was clear crystalline, thin but sturdy. Orla stood and examined this phenomenon of nature. Here was a vessel inside a tree, which prompted many questions in her mind that tumbled and jostled for answers, and as her mouth opened to pour out the litany of questions, Grace patted the young girl's hand and drew her forefinger to her closed lips to indicate silence. As the door to the vessel gradually slid open Orla's eyes widened as she observed the interior. The walls were sheer, like polished opaque glass but without the fragility of glass, with a space for two people to sit comfortably. They sat down on the crystal seats, which Orla reflected were surprisingly comfortable for such a hard material. Grace gave Orla a selection of tree bud remedies to drink which would help her to adjust to the change in atmosphere that she would feel when the vessel landed. She made several movements across a crystalline panel covered with dimple-like impressions – only initiates knew the touch sequence to activate the vessel – and almost immediately there was a feeling of movement, of floating upwards. Orla sat back and enjoyed the feeling of weightlessness and the remedies began to work relaxing her to the point where she was in a semi dream state but at the same time fully aware of her surroundings and her grandmother's words.

As an introduction to her initiation, Grace explained that the knowledge that the young princess was about to receive was obtained by visiting a place called Crystaland. It was the place from where the knowledge of the Eternal Wisdom of Creation came, a place from where her ancestors had come and integrated with the indigenous people of the island many thousands of years ago.

When the Crystalanders had come to Earth, they had great expectations of what their knowledge could bring and eventually, over thousands of years and many generational perfections, they had managed to produce purebred crystal-humans. Orla asked her grandmother why the Crystalanders had not stayed on Earth. Grace explained to her that during those early Crystaland days the Earth had truly flourished. The Earthlings had been given the Crystaland Gifts of Wisdom, they had become responsible tenants of their planet, and life had continued happily for all. When the Crystalanders were confident that Earth was safe and in good hands, they had slowly retreated so that they could continue their important work in other parts of the cosmos.

However, they had one major concern, whilst they believed Earthlings were competent to look after the planet, the cosmic travellers who had introduced the humanoids to earth had never been identified. When they had been conducting their initial reconnaissance of the planet they had discovered that the apocalypse, which had occurred before the last ice age, had destroyed all information about the humanoids' origins so their full genetic makeup was unknown and therein lay the flaw. And so, whenever the Crystalanders paid secret visits to Earth to monitor progress, they watched for indications of behaviour from the old primitive ways. Sure enough after thousands of years, it eventually began to resurface; slowly at first, and then it grew in momentum. At that point the Crystalanders knew that they had to retreat completely; they knew what was going to happen, as they had seen it many times before. Their role was never to act as permanent caretakers: they gave planets gifts for their development and then it was up to the inhabitants to cultivate them. Whenever a planet's inhabitants stopped using the Crystaland knowledge, the Crystalanders had to wait until the cycle of destruction turned full circle before their Wisdom could be requested again. But they were confident that the crystal memory would stay dominant in those people of the island ensuring that, as long as the islanders survived, the Wisdom of Creation would be protected for all time on Earth.

THE DIAMOND ELDERS

As Grace finished her story Orla pondered on what she had been told. She had never before really thought about the world outside of her island and she was now gaining the first insight of what happened when the Crystaland Laws of Wisdom were not followed. Orla's thoughts were distracted as she felt a slight feeling of descent, her stomach fluttered with excitement and the vessel came to a soft halt. They had landed in Crystaland.

The door to the crystal vessel slid open quietly and Orla immediately shot her hands up to cover her eyes as light intensely flooded her vision. The brilliance was dazzling and it took Orla a few moments to adjust her vision before she could step completely out of the vessel. She slowly removed her hands from her eyes and stepped forward gingerly trying to identify where the brilliant light was coming from but there was no beginning, end or interruption, the light was all around her. She looked down and as her eyes adjusted to the brightness she saw that she was standing on a path of clear white crystal rock flecked with small shards of gold. Her body began to vibrate lightly and tingle simultaneously, slightly unnerving her. As she began to see further afield with increasing clarity, she could see either side of the path and, as far as the eye could see, the terrain was covered in a fine white crystalline powder. Orla had experienced the brilliance of crystals before but this crystal was unlike anything she had ever witnessed. Either side of the path was a sea of white crystal dust which extended uninterrupted towards the horizon, eventually meeting up with the pure-blue sky, free from clouds or differing shades of blue, encasing the brilliance of the sun which was reflected in all of the crystal forms in that terrain.

Orla's attention came back to the path and she saw that her grandmother was communicating non-verbally but fluently with two graceful unicorns that had come to meet them. Orla had seen pictures of unicorns and had been told stories about them, but it had not prepared her for the feeling that she had when she met them. They were gentle and graceful yet, paradoxically, projected an enormous sense of power, intelligence and strength. Grace explained to Orla that the unicorns were to be their guides on their journey and that the gold, which flecked the path, was the element that allowed Orla to walk on the white crystal and still retain her balance. Orla was still dazzled by the uninterrupted white crystal, when her unicorn stroked her arm gently with the side of his head avoiding touching her with his horny protrusion. He communicated with her – amazingly she understood him – and explained that the vibration of the crystal was so strong that only humans who had been initiated into Crystaland could walk on the pure crystal terrain. Orla was amazed that she was now able to understand the non-verbal communication from the unicorn and was both comforted and surprised by the intimacy and trust that she felt towards this magical equine being.

Unlike most humans, although she had no fear-programming in her present life memory, the amount of new information that she was having to assimilate on every level of her understanding was a little confusing, so her new equine companion was a truly welcome addition to the travelling group. Before they set out on their journey Grace gave Orla some golden silk-like slippers made from pure gold thread. Orla explored them with her sensitive fingers and enquired whether they would be strong enough to walk on the crystal path. Grace reassured her that because they were made of gold metal spun finely like thread to look like silk, that they were strong enough to act as a buffer and stabiliser from the rapid vibration of the crystal. Whilst Orla slipped out of her day shoes and put on the new gossamer-thin gold slippers, she noticed that her grandmother was wearing white crystal slippers. At this point Orla was having to grapple with a number of confusing concepts and decided to leave the question of her grandmother's slippers until later – in the scheme of things crystal slippers were a minor detail. The small group began their journey continuing along a very long winding crystal path and with each step she felt a surge of energy pass through her feet into her body. With each step there was a reprogramming of her cells that allowed her to resonate deeper with the Wisdom from the diamond white crystal, which until now had lain dormant in her memory.

The little travelling group were eventually met by ten females who were of an ill-defined age, white haired and white clothed with piercing silver grey eyes and, like the crystal, had an overwhelming sense of brilliance radiating from each of them. Grace introduced Orla to the Diamond Elders who greeted the child, each one embracing her warmly. As Orla adjusted her vision again and was able to see through the brilliance that each woman projected, she noticed that these females all bore a strong resemblance to her family. With this strong feeling of familiarity, she immediately felt that she had come home; a feeling of peace and deep love resonated within her, eventually transforming to a soaring joy and exhilaration in her heart.

The Elders greeted Grace with an immense warmth and fondness as they had met with her many times during her human lifetime. They sat Orla on a diamond crystal and gold chair whilst they and her grandmother sat on pure diamond crystal chairs. Orla felt immediately that, although this crystal looked similar to those on Earth, it was a very different substance; the vibration was incredibly different which took a lot of adjustment for her young body. Every part of her body seemed to be jiggling and moving and vying for attention from each other, at the same time bringing an inner awareness of the subtle functioning of all the systems of the body. Equally, her mind was becoming hypersensitive and she was aware of the reactions in her brain to all the new stimulation both internally and externally. And, at the point where every part of her felt as if it had been stretched beyond its physical and mental capacity, there was a complete change of gear in her mind and, quite spontaneously, she experienced calmness gently washing over her. She was not resisting the diamond crystal anymore and her body had adapted sufficiently to enable her to assimilate the new information she was about to receive. The Elders explained to her that the purpose of the initiation was to fully activate the Crystaland memory in every cell of her body and her memory so that she would be able to straddle the two worlds of Earth and Crystaland. More importantly, she would be protected from the degenerative process of human fear. The destructive fear memory that every human carried within the deep emotional programming would be completely transformed. That is not to say that she would take silly risks with her safety, but that she would know only Wisdom and Wisdom-based discernment, and would always be an embodiment and reflection of the Wisdom of Creation.

The Elders began to unfold her story. She learnt that she carried the pure gene of Crystaland and therefore was able to reawaken to the Wisdom that the Crystaland Guardians had given to mankind. To stimulate the awakening that was stored deep in every cell of her body and her mind, it would be necessary for her to complete a series of journeys. Although Orla was truly grateful, as she knew that this was indeed a great honour, she did wonder why it was necessary for her to undertake such journeys, as she had been promised at birth in a sacred ritual to follow the rules of the island completely and never to deviate from the Crystaland teachings. The women gazed fondly at this young girl on the brink of womanhood, who had not yet the understanding of the complexities of mankind. She was still in that pure state of innocence, which was so rare for a human. Whilst they knew she would follow the ancient rules without question, the information stored in her memory, in her mind and in every cell of her body, had to be transformed completely in order for her to connect with Crystal Wisdom. This would then allow her to initiate others and be strong enough to withstand the resistance of the negative forces plaguing Earth.

The Elders finally told her that the time was coming for her to fulfil a role that was her destiny. Orla eagerly enquired of the Elders what that role would be. They smiled and told her that for the moment it was not appropriate for her to know but, by the time her journeys through all the worlds of Crystaland were complete, she would totally understand everything. She stared at them with the impatience of youth and asked: "Could I not have a clue?"

Her grandmother looked incredulously at her granddaughter who seemed to have totally forgotten where she was and with whom she was speaking. They smiled at her innocence once again and explained that if they told her now, such was her stage of development that she would not fully understand. With each journey she would uncover and assimilate more and more knowledge and, when she was ready, her destiny would present itself. Orla accepted this, as she knew these women were no ordinary women; from every vortex of their being they exuded wisdom, knowledge, love, peace, grace and authority. Such nurturing and respect was beautiful and overwhelming to the point that Orla totally forgot everything else and allowed herself to be immersed in the wonderful all-embracing feeling of complete trust.

A solemnity came upon the group and the Elders led Orla to what looked like an opal-coloured rectangular structure which Orla thought looked like a large king-size bed. Surrounding the opal were crystal diamonds with an opening of gold. The senior member of Elders led her to the gold step where she stood for a while feeling the now familiar warmth of the gold surge through her aligning and energising every atom in her body.

She felt the connection with every cell in her body and

amazingly she could discern how each part of her body responded to the gold. She was then lifted effortless by all the women, who placed her in a horizontal position hovering over the large opal and diamond structure and gently lowered her. But, to her surprise, the opal wasn't solid, it consisted of a vapour-like substance, and she was gently immersed until her whole body was covered. Although she was being held firmly by the female hands, which were strong and reassuring, a fleeting panic flashed across her mind that she wouldn't be able to breath and maybe this was a process of dying, but she need not have worried, there was no difference to her breathing, in fact she could breath deeper and with more ease. Her lungs felt as if they were expanding exponentially with each breath and with each breath, she felt increasingly elated.

At the very point of extreme elation she began seeing, fleetingly before her eyes, images that were speeding by so fast that she couldn't define what they were – just an amazing kaleidoscope of colour, shapes and sparkles, rays of light and sound. Vertical rays of colour rained down like waterfalls and, as they hit the ground, the colour turned to crystal particles. As she observed the concert of colours she identified that each colour had its own sound. All of her senses were going beyond the human boundaries into a realm of experience that were impossible to describe adequately with words. It was so overwhelming that she stopped trying to understand what it all was or meant and, at that very moment, she opened her mind and her heart, and spontaneously began to absorb the information that was being transmitted to her deep emotional memory. She surrendered to the process, relaxed, and at that point lost consciousness.

When she awoke, she was sitting on a pure diamond crystal chair feeling very different. She looked down at her hands and on the second finger of her left hand sat the most exquisitely cut solitaire diamond set in a white gold band. She marvelled at the fire that danced inside this beautiful diamond. Grace touched her hand gently and told her that on each of her journeys she would receive a jewel which represented the authority of each world. Orla's first response was excitement but then she realised that with the beauty of the gems came responsibility and she had no idea at this stage what that would be, which she found a little annoying but mostly intriguing. The Elders explained that all the information of Crystaland had been awakened in her when they had projected into her memory images of the qualities of Crystaland as if she was watching a film in extreme fast forward mode. It was already in her memory but for it to be awakened, the visual part of her brain had to receive the information to bring it into her consciousness. However, that was just the first stage of her initiation. She would now have to start on the series of journeys to complete the reawakening.

The Elders informed her that the first journey would be to go through Crystaland itself. The cells of her body had been prepared for her to experience the many worlds of Crystaland that contained all the fundamental qualities of Wisdom, which were the basic building blocks of all Creation. The second journey would be to see and experience the gifts that the Crystalanders had bestowed on mankind. The third journey would be to witness in real time what had happened when mankind had turned his back on Crystal Wisdom.

Sadly for Orla, this was the end of the journey for her grandmother. Grace wouldn't be accompanying her further as she had completed this initiation many decades before and had continued throughout her life receiving further initiations from these wise Elders. Her grandmother's body now was more sensitive and she was finding it increasingly difficult adjusting to the Earth's degeneration. It was time for her to complete her cycle on Earth when she would be taken into the Crystaland inner circle for her final initiation, which would ultimately mean the gradual shedding of her human side. Orla's mother had known this would happen and had said her farewells to her beloved mother before Grace had left with Orla, knowing that she would be reunited with her mother whenever she went to Crystaland to meet with her mentors.

This was the promise that had been given to all mankind by the Crystalanders; those who kept the Crystaland legacy alive would live in perfection and beauty for eternity.

CHAPTER TWO

THE CRYSTAL PATHS

THE VIOLET AND TURQUOISE PATH

Orla was sad to say goodbye to her grandmother who she cherished, but she knew that this was not the end of their journey together, they would be reunited many times when Orla visited Crystaland over her lifetime. One unicorn left with Grace, and Orla and her unicorn began the second stage of the journey on the crystal path. Orla followed him with excitement tinged with a little sadness at leaving her grandmother but quickly immersed herself into the experience of moving forward.

Gradually, the path began to reduce in brilliance, loosing its incandescent white. In the near distance she could see a large circular opening, resembling a huge round window, and inside the opening the air was swirling in circular clockwise movements. Unicorn explained that it was necessary for them to go through this portal that would take them to the next level of their journey and led her through the moving circular opening. Orla obediently followed Unicorn and looked bemused as she saw part of him disappear in the swirling mist of the portal. As she stepped through the opening she felt a ripple-like shard of energy go through every organ and cell of her body. As soon as she moved into the portal she simultaneously emerged on the other side. She quickly scanned her body to see if it had changed and was quite reassured to see that everything appeared to be the same on the outside, even her clothes. She surveyed the new environment and stood still in amazement, drinking in thirstily every facet of this new terrain. They were still on a crystal path but the colour had changed to a startlingly beautiful violet and turquoise, mixed together and almost indescribable in their beauty, shaped into such a beautiful configuration it took her breath away. She had never witnessed such symmetry, balance and beauty on a vast scale before. This crystal was gentler on her eyes than the brilliant diamond crystal but it was still very luminous and strangely compelling. Her eyes were adjusting much faster and she felt a familiar shift go through her body that she identified as yet another cellular calibration.

Either side of the path the terrain looked similar to that of Earth but on closer inspection it wasn't. There was no water, no trees, no flowers, and no animals. The landscape either side was constructed of the finest crystal powder. But the crystal was not just powder; it was formed in shapes of different shades of violet and turquoise. Orla had never realised that these colours could have so many shades and hues and evoke such deep stirrings in her memory. The colours ranged from the palest violet and turquoise, which were so pale they had an ethereal quality, to the deepest and richest, powerful shades. Adding to the complexity of the terrain, the shapes were geometric and carved into the landscape giving the appearance of a well-manicured violet-turquoise crystal garden. As she looked further into the horizon, she could see circular building-like structures in the same crystal shades but couldn't think what their purpose could be; the climate was very even, the skies were clear and bright with an extraordinary violet overlay of colour, the temperature warm with no wind – no clouds nor rain – therefore requiring no form of housing. Unicorn explained to her that these structures were the places on each of the Crystal Worlds that held knowledge; they were called the Halls of Experiences. Unicorn observed her puzzled look and explained that, whilst walking through the different worlds she automatically awakened the Crystal Wisdom, but it was also important for her to learn how the qualities of each world had been misused by mankind and this information was stored in the Halls of Experiences. Such information had to be stored separately so that it did not contaminate the memory held in the crystal terrain.

Orla asked why this information had to be kept at all. Unicorn shook his head gravely and informed her that this knowledge had to be stored and communicated to the royal family so that they understood the potential of self-sabotage that was part of the human condition. Orla struggled with this concept and Unicorn explained to her that she had led quite a sheltered life and the concept of self-destruction and self-sabotage were alien to her but, even though it would be shocking, she would have to learn about man's potential for insatiable greed and its consequences.

When Orla went into the Halls she would be given information of the real situation on Earth and how it had degenerated. Unicorn knew that this would be a challenge but was heartened to remember that after she received all her information from all the Crystal Worlds she would then be walked through another history of mankind, the history of the gifts that had been given to man by the Crystalanders of Creation's pure joy and harmony reminding her of man's true potential; the ability to be a vehicle for the work of the Wisdom of Creation. Though man had regressed, the gifts were still there, lying dormant in his memory longing to be awakened.

They continued along the path and after a while something caught her attention and she stopped and listened. She thought she could hear something but could not quite identify the sound. Straining her ears, she then thought her mind was playing tricks on her, as she thought she could hear absolutely nothing. Unicorn observed her confusion and explained to her that what she was actually hearing was a sound that was beyond silence. She stared, blinked, thought for a while, and was about to ask a question when she stopped and reminded herself of the Diamond Elders' words: "all would be revealed at the right time when she was ready to understand".

As the path spread before them they came upon the first inhabitants of Crystaland since leaving the Diamond Elders. These beings were very tall – twice the size of Orla's father and mother. However, whilst they had the form of human men and women they were not. A deep glow flowed from them. Every part of their presence exuded an incandescent light but they looked solid because they had a three dimensional form, similar to a hologram. Whereas the Diamond Elders had a completely ethereal quality, these people looked solid but weren't, which was strangely confusing for the young apprentice. On closer inspection Orla could see that at the core of their form were violet and turquoise crystals releasing an energy field shaped in the form of the human body.

As she drew closer to these beings gathered in a large circle, she noticed that the air around them appeared to be moving in a spinning motion; small spinning random movements filled the space between each being. Finally, as she stopped close to the perimeter of the circle, they beckoned her to join them. She entered their circle and was immediately thrown off balance by something that she couldn't identify. Astonishingly, they spoke to her without words – these beings were definitely not human – and she was able to understand them with ease. They communicated with her mind and instructed her to surrender, to allow her body and mind to adjust so that she could fully absorb what was happening. She gradually regained her balance and focused her attention deeper into the circle; her ears gradually became attuned to the subtle vibration until she was able to identify the sounds.

At first the sound was slightly chaotic which she couldn't follow; it was as if every part of the terrain was throwing out sounds, each geometric shape had a different vibration and the more attuned she became to the sound the louder it became, to the point where she felt she needed to cover her ears. One of the beings gently removed her hands from her ears, held her in his energy-field arms so that she could surrender fully, and at that point she began to identify the beauty of the sound. This particular sound was actually being projected from the beings themselves, not through their voices but with their whole presence and their focus was on the spinning vortices of energy within the circle. As soon as she had fully surrendered to the sound she saw that out of the vortices of energy little crystals appeared which gently settled on the ground. She watched, mesmerised, as the whole process repeated itself over and over again as if by magic, the spinning vortices producing crystal. This was the crystal powder, the foundation of everything that existed on the worlds of Crystaland, that contained within each tiny grain of crystal the Creative Wisdom of Eternity.

The beings demonstrated to her that sound has the ability to change the movement and direction of energy. On Earth, atoms were the smallest particles of physical matter and were limited to the speed at which their energy was able to transmit, but on Crystaland the vortices of energy moved much faster allowing them to be more receptive to the direction of sound. She had not been aware that crystals could be so versatile but she was told that absolutely anything could be made with atoms of this crystal. And, in fact, at this level atoms did not have subatomic particles as she had been taught in her earth science studies, but that they were vortices of energy which vibrated at a tremendously high rate allowing them to be directed into shape by intention, sound and light, but most of all by utilising the atom's own memory. Within the vortex of each atom was stored the memory of everything that it had experienced from the beginning of time; each atom retained the memory of the beginning of Creation and from this memory all creative life flowed. For this reason, they stressed, it is vitally important to be able to read the atoms' memory correctly so that they could be utilised for their correct purpose. Equally, it was important not to interpolate onto the atom any thought or intention which was not conducive to its specific function. These atoms were like sponges and whatever they experienced they would retain, good and bad, and feed that information into anything to which it was connected.

At this stage Orla did not quite comprehend what they meant by 'bad' and Unicorn, recognising her confusion, realised that very shortly she would be receiving her first indications of what 'bad' meant and was ambivalent about how she would receive this information. Realising the extent of her ignorance of the world at large, Unicorn decided that she needed to receive this information gradually. This was the first princess who had been exposed to the cumulative horror which was the 22nd century, and it was far too obscene to digest in one sitting. Unicorn pondered on this and wondered what part of the ugly collection of facts would be appropriate at this time and decided that he would give her small snapshots of life on present day Earth as she went to each of the different worlds. The last Crystal World, of course, would show her the complete history of the Earth and how it had reached this epic stage in its evolution of destruction. He honestly didn't know where to start; there wasn't a primer for Earth's destruction, it definitely required an 'Adults Only' category of censorship. He decided to request the assistance of the beings from some of the worlds to help in choosing the information she needed to assimilate.

Orla continued to be mesmerised by the different sounds producing different shades and shapes of the violet and turquoise crystal. She bent down, touched the powder and immediately felt energised and began to see again a kaleidoscope of images, which whizzed by at a terrific speed, so fast that she couldn't discern or identify the images. The more she was able to absorb of this world, the more she could hear its music. Different sounds were coming from different parts of the landscape; the spaces between the land, the sky and the crystal beings, were all producing their own individual sound that blended fluently into subtle harmonies. The vortices of energy were capturing the sound and recording all movement, the story of the landscape with its every nuance of movement was echoed in the open spaces. Orla concentrated hard on what she was experiencing, trying to identify which part of the landscape was producing particular sounds but it was impossible, she was overwhelmed by the enormity and complexity of the information she was witnessing. There was no such thing as silence and no such thing as empty space. Whatever she physically connected with discharged memory; every inhalation of the air that she breathed was teeming with memory. The information imprinting was dynamic and spontaneous and Orla considered this sheer brilliance. The boundaries of her human limitations were beginning to dissolve and her expectations of possibilities increased a thousand-fold.

The crystal beings led her to one of the Halls of Experience which was designed in an unfamiliar geometric shape that she couldn't quite identify as she had never seen anything quite like this before. It was far too complex, created from none of the geometric shapes and their combinations that had appeared in the history of Earth. But, it was these geometric shapes which ensured that the information contained within the Halls stayed there and didn't seep out into the perfection of the Crystal Worlds. Orla followed the crystal beings inside the building, formed from the same violet-turquoise crystal. She quickly glanced around the room and tried once again to make sense of what she was seeing. The walls and ceiling were absolutely sheer and smooth creating a mirrored effect reflecting multiple layers of everything inside the interior of the Hall. Orla sat in front of one of the walls of sheer crystal and the beings communicated to her that she would now be shown why they had come to Earth.

And, as if watching a movie, she saw how these super beings took their crystal structures around galaxies, choosing planets that had fallen into disintegration and placed them in a particular formation on specific energy centres so that the planets could be calibrated and rebalanced in preparation for transformation. Earth was one of these planets.

Orla watched intently how they traversed the galaxies looking for planets that had signs of life that were conducive to their crystals – minerals that had a similar atomic structure. Whilst Earth's atomic structure was dense, it was still possible to develop and take it to the next level. Earth had gone through a catastrophic apocalypse and was barren, and had been barren for decades. The core of the Earth had been full of anger and had erupted causing catastrophic weather conditions that had caused the water levels to change, covering many landmasses. Eventually Earth had stopped roaring, cooled down, and an ice age followed where the earth was covered in a protective coating of ice allowing the minerals to rest, sleep and eventually regenerate. Time had healed and the minerals showed signs of wakening. The warmth began to seep through the Earth; the ice began to melt causing the seas to swell prompting landmasses to reconfigure into different continents and islands. The dangerous poisons that had once filled the air and contributed to the destruction of life on the planet had disappeared and the plant life had slowly started to emerge again; Earth was trying to rebirth itself. It was at this time that the Crystalanders felt the birth cries of the minerals of the Earth far into space and came to the planet to assist and recharge those atoms so that the cycle of evolution and transformation could begin once again.

All this information was overwhelming for Orla who was still in the innocence of her Crystal Island experience, but she absorbed it without question as she reminded herself once again that the Diamond Elders had reassured her that only at the end of her journeys in Crystaland would she have a complete understanding. Unicorn gazed at his charge and sighed with sadness. He could see how innocent this dear child was and he desperately wanted to protect her from the harshness that she would ultimately have to face. When this introductory experience was over the violet-turquoise beings gave Orla a ring made from the turquoise and violet crystal, which fitted on the little finger of her left hand. Orla looked down at the sparkling gem sitting next to the finger that bore her diamond ring thinking innocently that they went together rather well. At this stage she did not have an awareness of how important these rings would be to her in the future.

THE GREEN AND YELLOW PATH

And so her journey continued. Unicorn led her back to the path, which gradually changed from the violet-turquoise to an iridescent green-yellow crystal. The terrain stayed the same only the colour changed. The path was brighter than the landscape and as far as the eye could see the landscape was a vibrant green-yellow crystal, carved into the now familiar geometric shapes that seemed to vibrate the tiny crystals, forming a powdery covering over the shapes, giving the impression of a landscape constantly in motion. Orla eventually came upon a group of beings who shared the same colour hues as the landscape, but the colour was much brighter, almost neon. They were busily working the crystal powder into the geometric shapes:squares, diamonds, hexagrams, octagons, decagons and then amazing multidimensional forms of these, once again, none like she had seen on Earth. As in the violet-turquoise world, the beings were using sound to carve the facets of the shape, each tone carving a different facet. It was truly fascinating and beautiful. The whole process, whilst appearing complex, was accomplished with ease and confidence. The Crystalanders explained how sound changes the direction of energy. The Crystaland particles of energy moved much faster and became units of vibrating energy that had to be harnessed speedily and correctly by sound to transform them into the crystal powder and then into complex shapes. However, they emphasised that it was never appropriate to create random shapes, otherwise random memory would be implanted into the crystal powder. All the shapes had to follow a formula of construction and each atom had its own memory of what it was to be and do. Each shape was unique and each one made only if there was a specific requirement. Everything that was produced had to have a higher purpose and be a reflection of universal beauty and perfection. These shapes were the foundation of all matter and these beings were the architects of whatever needed to be formed in the material world.

Orla tried to absorb this concept and went back into her memory of her life on Crystal Island and her thoughts went to the Secret Garden where she had observed the plants and how the shapes of the fruits and the petals of the plants could be broken down to a geometric shape. The beings were pleased; they could see she was now beginning to relate what she was being taught in the Crystal worlds, to life on Earth. As had become the custom, the Crystalanders gave Orla a ring made from the green and yellow crystal, which fitted perfectly on her middle finger, giving her another tool to help her to relate the teachings of Crystaland to Earth.

Much as she had wanted to stay and explore this creative environment, Unicorn came to Orla and told her that she had to leave this world and move on as she had much to learn. She had already spent a year in Earth-time in this world. She was stunned, as time seemed not to matter and most definitely did not equate to Earth-time. Unicorn warned her that she had a limited amount of Earth years to complete her journey and he would be her guide as to how long she could spend in any one world. She realized how dependent she was on her mystical equine companion and that, such was the energy of Crystaland, she needed something or someone outside of herself to guide her progress; if all the stages were so fascinating and engaging she would never want to leave any of them.

THE SAPPHIRE AND SILVER PATH

Orla joined Unicorn on the path that gradually changed from the greenish-yellow, deepening to a sapphire-blue speckled with flecks of silver. As before, the terrain remained the same but it looked as if every shade of blue that there could possibly be was reflected in the crystal either side of the path, ranging from the palest blue to the deepest blue-black intermingled with flecks of silver. At the point at which the horizon touched the sky there seemed to be only a slight change in the gradation of blue, giving the impression that the sky and the landscape were one. On closer observation of the terrain, either side of the path, she could see that the crystal was formed into shapes, some familiar others too complex and completely indiscernible. The shapes were similar to letters; she recognised the Earth's alphabets and other ancient letters that she had also learnt but others she grappled to identify.

A group of sapphire-silver beings wafted towards her and greeted her warmly. She was becoming accustomed to the beings reflecting the colour of the surrounding crystal and was not at all surprised by their appearance. They took Orla off the path, which surprised Orla as she thought she was only able to walk on the paths. They reassured her that the more information she assimilated in each of the worlds, the easier it would be to walk in their terrains as every atom in her body was becoming cleansed of the human impediment – little as it was in Orla – allowing for the Crystal Wisdom to once again be prominent in her memory. The group moved to where other sapphire-silver beings were busy at work and demonstrated to her how letters and numbers were created.

Letters containing specific information, had been given to mankind to help them focus their intentions both verbally and inscribed. She had been taught all the ancient languages of Earth, but could not identify these letter forms. The beings explained that they were the precursors to all languages for all worlds that were inhabited by beings of limited intelligence. From these letters came the languages of the universes and within the shape of the letters carried the memory of Creation – language being essential in the process of maintaining the Wisdom of Creation.

Each letter had a different hue and glow and when put together into formulas of words, the subtle information emitted from the combined letters increased the power of the information released from the individual letters. But it was also emphasised that the organisation of these letters had to follow a specific formula otherwise the information would be confused, dissipated, and the meaning lost. By being able to read the information from each letter she was able to identify which letters complemented each other. She also saw the shapes of sounds – not the musical notes that she had learnt at home – but different shapes which were much more ornate and complex, and she realised that the musical notes she had learnt on the island were comparatively simplistic. Here again, by feeling the information of the shape she was able to formulate the correct sound. Because the Crystal Wisdom that governed sound, colour, and the vortex's own memory, was always strictly followed, only the most beautiful sounds were produced. There was never any waste – no discordant notes.

When the Crystalanders arrived on a primitive planet, they had to give the indigenous people the gift of language to help them communicate, and it was in this world that the languages of all the planets contained in all the universes were created. The Crystalanders had the ability to identify which language the inhabitants of the different planets would be able to master. This quality was necessary for helping the many species that they tried to rehabilitate who were of lower intelligence, as this was their only method of communication and therefore a necessary component for their progression.

As Orla walked further on the path she came upon sapphire-silver crystal formed in the shape of numbers. The sapphire beings explained to Orla that numbers were vital to all forms of Creation. Each number had a specific vibration, an energy value – even zero – and the number was all-important to any form to ensure that it was truly balanced and in keeping with the Wisdom of Creation. She learnt that sound was encrypted with a formula of numbers and from those formulas, geometric shapes were created. It took a specific focus of intention to achieve though, and to help her experience this the sapphire-silver beings took her to meet the Keepers of the Numbers. She was directed to a crystal pyramid structure in the blue and silver landscape and was led to a chamber with a crystal platform in the centre. Ten sapphire-silver crystal males appeared and encircled the stage. A spotlight shone from above the platform onto its centre and then spontaneously, numbers appeared in holographic form in front of each of the men. Orla could see that the men raised their arms and then directed the numbers to create formulas and, when these formulas were complete, a shape would appear in the spotlight in a multidimensional form. As soon as the shape was formed a sound was released into the room. As the sound echoed around the room, miraculously, she could identify with all her senses the information that was attached to the sound. The information was not three-dimensional or logical, it was a feeling that she experienced deep in her heart, of beauty and love and she wanted to perpetuate this feeling within her forever. Orla thought this surely was the cleverest thing she had seen and, to the surprise of Unicorn, spontaneously clapped her hands with glee when the sound ceased. She could have spent endless days being mesmerised by these beings orchestrating formulas, shapes and then sound, over and over again.

The beings smiled at her and, as was the tradition, gave her a ring made from the silver-flecked sapphire crystal which they ceremoniously placed on her index finger. Orla enquired as to the quality of the silver as it was a metal not crystal. They explained to her that the silver was very reactive and was able to hold the form of letters and numbers more securely in the body of the sapphire crystal. Without this, the information emitted from the sound could not be translated to the material world in a form that would be understood. Orla reflected on her small collection of rings and looked at each one representing the qualities of the Crystal Worlds from where they had come, an ever-present reminder of her journey so far.

Before she left this world, Unicorn and the beings took her to one of the Halls of Experience. As she walked closer to the Hall, she observed its perfect crystalline dome-like structure created from the sapphire crystal and silver, which had the shapes of the languages and music carved around the exterior of the Hall. She followed Unicorn through the semi-circular opening and, although there was no door, as she stepped over the threshold she sensed a difference in the atmosphere. Her focus changed from the chamber to her interior self, it was as if she was looking inside her own mind, being drawn to the deeper recesses of her memory, which prompted her to close her eyes and experience rather than understand. Unicorn nudged her forward gently with his head and guided her towards a crystal seat in front of a sheer crystal screen. Two beings from this world, sensing her need for reassurance, gently sat either side of her and she immediately felt a strong sense of security from them both and began to relax, releasing her mind as she prepared to receive the next chapter of Earth's story

The screen began to change and images appeared before her; images of people in many situations, in the workplace, at home, at school, all of whom were in a state of anxiety and anger, treating each other in an aggressive or disrespectful manner. This appalling behaviour was reflected in all levels of societies and in all countries of the planet. There was such a sense of fear pervading the lives of everyone that respect fell to the bottom of the list of criteria for relationships. She was amazed at the degree of vitriol that people could produce. Equally the language was appalling; she saw what appeared to be educated adults throwing ugly words at each other, which had the effect of filling the memory of the air with sadness. Not only were the people dealing with each other in their daily lives like this, but it was also reinforced and reflected in their entertainment. Life was imitating art and art had become truly ugly. The content of the entertainment industry was dedicated to depicting the most base form of human relationships, portraying characters with limited personality traits, functioning on superficial levels thereby affirming and imprinting that limited and primitive standard of behaviour deeper into the minds of its audience. Man had become obsessed with bringing to the surface his most base behaviour, and was addicted to watching it over and over again so that it constantly overwrote all Crystal knowledge ensuring no challenge to authority.

The music also reflected the same ugliness, people with no access to the songs of Wisdom – the music of Creation – controlled the production of music and the result was another reflection of the ugly base behaviour. Because of the advancing technology, much of the popular music which poured out of personal music systems, could be manufactured and therefore distort the ability of music to convey the message of Crystal Wisdom. Power leaders decided to minimise the use of people with true musical talent for a very good reason; these gifted musicians were true communicators of the Crystal knowledge and their music would speak to the Crystal Wisdom hidden deep in the memory of man, awakening his thirst for more Wisdom. Like every other industry in the 22nd century, the priority of the music industry was to make money and control the buying power of the consumer. With this intention they succeeded in creating sounds that tapped into the primitive side of man leaving behind in its wake another agenda, which Orla would only fully comprehend on her last journey and was shown the Earth's history in all its dark glory. She was far from ready to be able to witness the enormity of that information at this stage.

Orla was puzzled and wondered why and how the beauty of Creation's sound had been distorted so much that it was not identifiable. On Crystal Island the voices of the people were naturally musical, lyrical and nurturing, which served to reinforce the balance and communion they had with nature. The melodies of Creation that were created in the turquoise and violet crystal, had been lost in a cacophony of angst. The screen became blank and there was complete silence in the chamber. With a sigh of disappointment, Orla stood up wearily and bade farewell to the crystal beings as she slowly left the chamber following Unicorn back onto the crystal path deep in reflective thought about the scenes that she had just witnessed.

THE RUBY AND IRON PATH

They continued silently on their path as Orla contemplated the complexity of the multilayered information she was receiving. The crystal path again began to change colour, gradually losing the blue tones, adding warmer tones until it changed to a deep ruby red flecked with a dark metal that she couldn't quite discern. They were eventually greeted this time by very different beings, beings with much more physical presence. Within their core was a ruby crystal, but their outer form took on a more solid human appearance. Men and women with a physically very strong appearance greeted her. Their muscles were well defined, their limbs long and they had coarse red curly hair – every shade of red that Orla had ever seen. Her attention was drawn to a group of them who were engaged in what looked like combat but there was no physical contact. They were using their minds to deflect the other person. They could use their mind to move, elevate and lift objects, and do any physical task they were called upon to do.

Unicorn emphasised the importance of the qualities of strength in mind and body that the Crystalanders needed when they travelled the galaxies, as they had to be able to deal with all kinds of resistance from the indigenous beings they encountered. Orla enquired as to the nature of the dark metal flecked throughout the ruby crystal and Unicorn explained to her that, for the ruby Crystalanders to have physically strong structures which would allow them to traverse hostile planets, they needed a metal called iron to give them the strength and magnetic resonance of three-dimensional worlds. She knew about the effects of iron on the human body and knew of its importance for human blood. What she didn't know was that it was the iron in the blood that carried the messages from the Crystal memory to all parts of the body so that there was a constant flow of information being received by all the body's cells.

It was also the ruby Crystalanders who decided on the quality of information to be given to the planets that they successfully colonised. These pioneering Crystalanders would visit a planet, interact with the primitive inhabitants and discern what information they could cope with. To give too much knowledge at once could confuse and overwhelm them, to give too little could hinder their development. Orla was mesmerised watching their disciplined movements. There was no competition amongst them just strong, focused discipline and a deep respect for each other. As she was watching this wonderful display of strength, one of the ruby beings came towards her with a necklace made from a string of ruby crystal. Each crystal was mounted into an iron claw and was held together by an iron coupling. He gently placed the necklace around her neck where it sat comfortably, settling into the hollow curve between her neck and collarbone. She closed her eyes, felt the strength course through her body from the crystal and iron, and smiled in deep gratitude as she became acutely aware of the protective quality that this necklace gave her. She was gradually gaining a better insight of what life was like in the world outside of Crystal Island and she intuitively knew that she would need this protection one day.

Whilst she sat with her eyes closed experiencing the newfound strength flow through her body, she gradually became aware of another person in her mind. She opened her eyes and saw a group of young men undergoing training from the ruby Crystalanders but one of them looked very familiar. She blinked her eyes in an effort to make her see more clearly and then, with great delight, she recognised Finn. It was not the Finn she had left behind but an older Finn. Since they had been separated to follow their own initiations, he had grown in both height and physique. She watched admiringly how well he demonstrated his physical and mental strength. When the group had finished, she walked over to him shyly as he was now a grown man, not a boy, and she still viewed herself as young girl completely unaware of how she had also developed. He too was surprised by her appearance when she approached him. She had grown even more beautiful and her experiences in the Crystal worlds had given her an air of authority and majesty, which left him speechless and breathless. They embraced awkwardly and surveyed each other. Their thoughts were united and each understood the other's hesitancy. Orla broke the spell and began to ask him many questions about what he had learnt and how long he had been on ruby Crystaland, and within minutes they were back to their old animated selves, talking rapidly and excitedly together. After a period of time Unicorn came over to the charmed couple and indicated that Orla had to have an understanding of how the world had misused the ruby crystal energy. Finn nodded, he had already seen this, and more, as part of his initiation and had been both shocked and deeply disappointed. He knew Orla needed to understand the degeneration of the planet but his protective side wanted to shield her from the harshness of the world. She hugged Finn farewell as he, like her, still had several Crystal years more of his initiation to complete, and Unicorn led her to the ruby Hall of Experiences. As with the other Halls, the ruby Hall was made of ruby crystal bedecked with iron configured into shapes, which represented the atomic structure of iron, but Orla could see that the structure was far more complex than that which she had learnt at her studies.

Just as she was immersing herself into the complexity of the atoms trying to understand their structure, the ruby crystal beings led her to a seat in front of the crystal screen. Within minutes images filled the screen of horror and devastation, depicting scenes of destruction made by sophisticated arms that could annihilate whole countries with the press of one button by one man. Each Federation on Earth had their own armoury of destruction and, in their childlike attempt to control, would send missiles of destruction into the lives of innocent people destroying their future completely in one moment of angry leadership. The images on the screen eventually stopped and Orla, once again, hung her head in disappointment; she couldn't understand the degree of hatred that humans could project on to each other. Looking at the ruby beings she asked them: "Don't they realise that the hatred that they project onto others is transferred back onto themselves?" They confidently assured her that, when the time came, she would see how this had come to pass in the world and therefore understand what would be required for it to be transformed. She accepted this explanation with humility and wanted to stay longer to ask many, many questions but Unicorn led her out of the Hall and gently reminded her that she still had a long way to go before completing her journey.

THE CORAL PATH

As they left ruby Crystaland, the path began its familiar process of changing colour, lightening in shade, and eventually becoming a rich coral crystal; not the bright orange of the sun, but a soft rose coral. The landscape either side was smooth and orderly. There were no rough crystals on this landscape just a smooth crystalline structure reflecting the strong rays of its three suns. The crystals deflected the heat from the three suns of Crystaland back into the atmosphere so that the ground didn't absorb the intense heat of the suns but benefited from their brilliance. The combination of the three suns on the coral crystal increased the intensity of the release of information from the crystals so that they were teeming with activity and information. Orla felt her mind become acutely sharp and alert. She felt as if all her senses were heightened, but not with the normal jagged energy that usually accompanied humans whose senses were heightened because of fear. This was an acute elevation of her senses to their optimum level feeling that each one was working in harmony, complementing and enhancing the others.

As before, the beings that greeted her reflected the colour of the terrain but unlike the beings from the other worlds, they communicated with her verbally and explained that they were responsible for teaching language to the inhabitants of the selected planets they colonised. They had the responsibility of identifying the language that the inhabitants would best be able to assimilate and use. She had already witnessed in the other worlds the rules governing the combining of numerology with language, sound, colour, and light, which formed the basis of all Creation, but all this had to be put into a formula that new colonies could understand. The indigenous people were then taught how to apply the necessary focus and discipline that was required to communicate the Crystal knowledge. These formulas were the foundation of the Crystal Wisdom and the basis for all science and technology on Earth that would be developed in the fullness of time.

Unfortunately, Orla would eventually discover the full impact of what happened if these rules were broken but, before she left this world, Unicorn led her to the coral Hall of Experiences which initially Orla could not see in the landscape as the suns' rays were bouncing off its dome shape causing the Hall to merge into the landscape. The coral beings joined her and, as before, sat her before the crystal screen which began to fill with images of children. Orla stared at the screen in disbelief she was witnessing large numbers of children maybe 2,000 or more in large concrete buildings called schools, segregated into rooms of about sixty children with one teacher. Each schoolroom had a security officer with various weapons to 'control' the class. The beings explained to her that the cities had become so overpopulated that there was insufficient money for smaller schools so they herded children together where they stayed for seven hours a day. The schools were cramped; ill lit, with poor ventilation and heating. It was little more than crowd control rather than the educating of young precious minds. More interestingly, she thought, was what they were being taught. She looked on questioningly as she heard teachers giving definitions of the beginning of the Earth and she laughed and asked Unicorn if this really was a fairy story they were telling the children. Unicorn shook his head solemnly and waited for the crystal beings to educate Orla. They explained to her that all Crystal knowledge had been suppressed and mankind had decided that they were the co-creators based on limited three-dimensional knowledge. She gasped; even Orla knew from her experience that by following this path of education, it restricted the ability of an individual to speak their truth. At a very early age, these young humans were being conditioned not to question, not to find their own inner gift and accept the word of the so-called 'man-made authority'. Orla pondered: *If the children are educated in this way, what sort of contribution could they make to the welfare of the planet if they were not using their gifts?*

Orla reflected on her own education. In a child's early years on Crystal Island they learnt about the qualities of the Gifts of Wisdom by experiencing them. So they spent their days exploring the landscape, learning to create sound, drawing and painting what they saw and being taught to align their thoughts with nature.

The main subject on the curriculum was learning the language of Creation and developing personal gifts and talents for its continuation. Once this was established then the knowledge of the three-dimensional world was learnt in a very short space of time. As they matured, their ability to learn facts were accelerated and they could absorb information by just looking once at a page of a book or the screen of a computer.

The beings instructed her to look at the screen again and she saw how industrialisation – the manufacture of 'things and stuff' – had gobbled up the countryside and, where there once stood lush fields and productive farms, now stood cities, towns and large buildings where people were employed in virtually the same conditions as the schools. However, there was no need for the security guards to keep control in the workplace. The fear of unemployment kept the people in a vice-like grip of obedience. Sadly, their imprisonment, which had begun at school, continued seamlessly from school to work. This saddened Orla as she felt she was witnessing the imprisonment of people from the age of five till they died with a very primitive range of understanding.

"Which was of course", interjected Unicorn, "the intention of the leaders at that time. No free thinking, no creativity – no challenge. The survival formula of the power leaders".

Orla thought seriously about this but it was hard for her to understand given that her upbringing on Crystal Island was based on respect for each person's natural gifts and talents; their whole life was dedicated to exploring and expanding upon their gifts. Unicorn knew that she would eventually be able to piece the whole picture together and understand the global impact of industrialisation. Orla and Unicorn left the Hall, and the coral Crystalanders gave Orla a gift of coral earrings that she could wear whenever she needed to have dialogue with anyone programmed with fear. The coral would help her to sift through the confusion of their fear, give her clarity and be able to talk to them in words that would not challenge their inner safety.

THE EMERALD AND COPPER PATH

Unicorn led Orla back to the path, which would lead her to the penultimate Crystaland world. The path progressed from the deep coral to a rich emerald green crystal flecked with the metal copper. The terrain either side of the path reflected the colours of the path forming continuous fields of crystalline powder. The beauty of the combination of the colour of the crystal coupled with the metal was both overwhelming and intoxicating. She felt as if she wanted to run deep into the landscape, immersing herself in the richness of the colours. In the distance she saw a large beautiful pure emerald green crystal structure – the size of a castle – glistening in the dazzling light from the white sun. This was larger than the other Halls of Experience and Unicorn suggested that for this part of the journey she should ride on his back to help her adjust to the very different energy she was going to experience. He bent one of his front legs, outstretched the other, and bowed his head so that she could clutch on to his thick mane to mount his back easily. Unicorn advised her to stay on his back until she was greeted by the beings of this world. The vibration of this world was very different from the previous worlds and she needed to be introduced to it gradually.

As they went through the entrance, she was filled with the glory and beauty of the structure of the emerald crystal forms that appeared to embrace and envelop her. Beautiful geometric shapes were carved into the high walls and ceiling of the building, but within those geometric shapes were smaller shapes made from copper. On the outside, the walls appeared as sheer as glass but internally the building was a vortex of energy radiating from the shapes engraved into the surfaces. Unicorn explained that the addition of the copper boosted and stabilised the energy of the emerald crystal and, sensing the very different atmosphere, Orla realised that, had she not been on Unicorn's back she would have had great difficulty concentrating and would have been physically and mentally overwhelmed.

She was eventually welcomed by incredibly beautiful crystal beings with more human form than the beings from the previous worlds. They were luminous jade green in colour, with luxuriant deep golden shining hair and eyes the colour of copper. They greeted Orla and instructed her to dismount so that she could be led around the building. She dismounted Unicorn and was guided around the walls. The beings indicated to her to touch each of the geometric shapes on the walls, and with each shape she received a feeling which was something between a mild electric shock and a pulse of warmth, but she was able to feel it in different parts of her body. Each shape seemingly connected to a specific organ of her body. Unicorn, sensing that she was beginning to feel overwhelmed by the many sensations in her body, reassured her that this was the route of initiation, which was required before going into the main chamber of the building.

After completing a circuit of the walls, she eventually entered the vast inner chamber. The walls were sheer so that they reflected each other creating a palpable cross exchange of energy. The vibration began to work through her body so forcefully that she thought she would begin to elevate. She felt the familiar feeling of confusion and resistance whereupon Unicorn encouraged her to surrender to that feeling. As she became accustomed to the vibration, she began to move but she wasn't walking, she looked down and saw that she was hovering just above the ground which enabled her to move with more speed. In the centre of the chamber there appeared to be a waterfall that spilled over a gigantic emerald crystal into a pool of what looked like jade liquid discharging a neon glow.

She approached the waterfall and two female beings dressed in fine green crystalline robes, removed her cotton dress and gave her a loose robe similar to theirs that had been manufactured from the powdered emerald crystal interlaced with strands of copper. Even though the cloth of the garment was spun from crystal and metal, it was surprisingly soft, and light as the finest silk. They led her into the pool and placed her under the waterfall. To her surprise, the substance was not heavy, or wet or suffocating, it just enveloped her entire body, seeping through every pore into the deepest parts of every organ, bone and muscle, until she felt that she was glowing all over, inside and out. She had never felt so well and vibrant. She was young and had very few ailments but, like all humans, she became tired at times, mentally and physically, and the growing experience had not been without discomfort.

When it was time, she was led out of the waterfall and was given new robes. These robes were made from the same emerald crystal and copper and were to be used whenever she went into the crystal circle on Crystal Island. The combination of wearing these robes within the crystal circle would ensure that her physical body was guaranteed continued health even though she would be exposed to high levels of pollution, both mentally and physically when she began her work. Unicorn stared at her and smiled deeply from within his heart. He could see that this world had given her the cellular strength needed for the final journey. This world held the knowledge of the regeneration for all the atoms that formed Crystaland and every cell in Orla's body had now been energetically enhanced far beyond that of humans. With that change came subtle changes in her physical appearance.

THE GOLDEN PATH

Unicorn once again gathered up Orla as it was time to continue on the final journey of Crystaland and he observed her changed appearance. Like all the young royal women she had porcelain skin, hazel eyes, and dark hair. Her skin was now becoming more transparent, her eyes losing the brown of the hazel and becoming more green, and her hair had a few strands of the telltale white which came about every time a royal human body went through an initiation. She was reluctant to leave but he reassured her that, because all that she had experienced was now active in her memory, she would be able to visit the different worlds of Crystaland at anytime. With that reassurance, she happily proceeded onto the final path, which began to change the further they walked. This time the path changed to a strong golden crystal and her spirits were immediately uplifted. This was a colour that she could not comprehend. She was familiar with the precious metal gold but this was gold crystal. Not yellow, orange, or red but gold. This crystal had a depth unlike any other of the crystals she had experienced – a cross between a metal and crystal. This was the pathway to the knowledge of all beauty, the beauty of Creation, the wonder of Creation, a true reflection of the creative process. This was where all the qualities of the previous worlds came together and performed in perfect harmony.

The terrain either side of the path was also different. Instead of one colour being the theme of this world, all the different colour crystals from all the crystal worlds were present, moving with the sound that was bouncing from the landscape. The sounds were beautiful, the shapes were amazing, the colours incredibly pure and intense. Everything was a symphony of sound, colour, shape and light. There were no discordant notes, no odd shapes, only balance. She felt an overwhelming sense of splendour and beauty, which brought the young Orla to tears of joy. "This is truly perfection" she beamed.

She stepped off the path following Unicorn and hesitated slightly to feel the reaction of the crystals in her body, but there was no interruption, she was able to walk off the path directly onto the crystal terrain. She moved fluently through the different colours and shapes as they were not material, they were an accumulation of different levels of vibrating vortices that created the crystals.

Each colour gave her a different sensation, different information and a different perspective. She felt every cell of her body was resonating with every vortex of the universe. She was the colours, she was the sounds, and she was the shapes. She lost touch with her own body and became part of all and everything around her. Each colour pulsated its quality into her body. She was beyond flesh and blood and had totally activated her crystal memory. She was able to communicate to all the beings from all the different worlds without words. She could move the shapes with her mind and equally, change the colours of the shapes with her mind. Her mind reached out and touched the most ancient and sacred teachings of the universe expanding exponentially according to her increased expectation, removing any vestige of human limitation. Every part of her memory system of both mind and body had been completely reprogrammed.

A group of beings from this world came to greet her. These were the most human looking of all the beings that she had encountered on this journey. They were statuesque, with golden hair, luminous white skin, and silver-grey eyes. They explained that they were the beings that biologically integrated with humans and stayed on Earth guiding mankind through its infancy of Crystaland evolution. Orla stared intently at these golden beings and sensed a real familiarity with them, as if she had known them all her life. Then in flash of realisation she knew that these were her ancestors. The part of them that was within her had been completely awakened and she spontaneously hugged them with a deep sense of belonging. The gift they gave Orla was a large ornate golden crystal ring, which fitted on the middle finger of her right hand. The crown of the ring had a geometrical shape carved into it, which was a graphic representation of her name and her title. This was the ring of Responsibility that all female members of the royal family received after their first initiation. With this ring she was able to access and integrate all the knowledge from all the Crystal worlds and from now on would only conduct herself with pure Crystal Wisdom. She had successfully completed the transformation – 80 per cent Crystal and 20 per cent human.

CHAPTER THREE

THE GIFTS

By this time in her journey, Orla was feeling a stronger sense of purpose. Whilst she had been in a totally receptive mode going through the different worlds, she was now eager to move on to fully understand how those creative qualities she had experienced were translated into the Crystal Gifts that were given to mankind.

And so, without a moment's rest she started on the next stage of her journey. Unicorn explained that she would now discover the unique gifts that the Crystalanders had created for planet Earth so that it could once again flourish and continue on its path of transformation. He told her that she needed to experience the gifts, not just watch them on a screen, as it was the experience that triggered the awakening of the gifts in her memory. Again her journey would follow a crystal path that would walk her directly through the story of Earth's rebirth.

THE GIFT OF ENERGY

She mounted her Unicorn with eagerness and the golden
crystal path began to deepen in colour and eventually
changed to a deep, earthy maroon crystal. Either side of
the path the terrain was magnificent, rich soil, lush plants,
and tall strong trees similar to those that she had seen in
the Secret Garden. Orla was walking through the first years
of the fruition of the gifts. The Earth looked magnificent;
nature was decked out in all her finery. As they travelled
on the path Unicorn continued with the story of the
Crystalanders' arrival on the planet. The Earth had settled
down from its chaos and the Crystalanders recognised
that the soil was suitable for adding new minerals to
increase its yield. There was an abundance of water on the
planet; the regular rainfall washed through the rich soil
taking with it the important minerals that would find their
way into the springs and rivers providing rich healing
properties for human bodies and also regenerating the
soil. This, coupled with the seasonal balanced climate, was
a perfect formula for creative life. And so the experiment
began.

   As Orla travelled along the crystal path she saw that the
Crystalanders had brought their own colonisation crystals
to start the reprogramming. This diamond shaped crystal,
when placed in the waters, released new minerals, which
then bonded with the Earth's original minerals and formed
new compounds that were to form the new life on Earth.
The young princess watched as the Crystalanders appeared
on her island, surprised at how primitive it looked, and
to her horror, the people looked equally primitive. But
the Crystalanders took the large crystal diamond shapes
and placed them in each lake or river on the island and,
as soon as the inhabitants of the island drank the water,
a change started to take effect in their bodies. The magic

had begun to work. The minerals washed through their bodies and released the negative blockages in their cells allowing a pathway to be established for the knowledge that would eventually be given to them to be absorbed without resistance. The Crystalanders then took the large crystal columns, which were dotted in a haphazard fashion around the planet, and placed them in a circle on the Earth's energy centres – these were places where the mineral formation was latticed in a more complex pattern – and finally added their crystals to boost the power of the indigenous crystals. The calibration of the energy centres was complete.

Because of their vibrational structure, these supra beings could never leave a group behind to oversee the planet indefinitely. They would not have survived, as the planet's vibration would always be too dense for the finely balanced energy of the Crystalanders. In Crystaland the smallest particle was a vortex of energy, on Earth, the vortices were encased in an atom with physical structures so that its information may be utilised in a material world – a world of physical form. They therefore had to make sure that the gifts they gave Earth fulfilled all of the planet's needs and were given in a way that they were never forgotten. So they set about identifying what these people needed, not just to survive but also to evolve into their universal intelligent potential.

THE GIFT OF HEALTH

The crystal path changed again, this time to a deep green crystal and around Orla the terrain became a sea of plants, flowers, bushes and trees which oozed resins and gums from their trunks. The smells were intoxicating; sweet, floral and musk notes competed with the bitterness of the herbs. Unicorn continued narrating Earth's story. The Crystalanders had provided every plant for human health. They had recognised the primitive biological systems of the humanoid and seen how quite easily the cells degenerated leaving their bodies vulnerable to disease. At the point that the Crystalanders came to Earth, the average life span of a humanoid was twenty-one years, so it was necessary to provide for them plants for both nutrition and medicine.

In this terrain, Orla recognised plants that she had seen growing on her island but these plants were more lush – even the plants in the Secret Garden could not compare with these first generation plants. There was one plant in particular that she recognised which would give humans all the protein they required so that they never needed to eat flesh; the flesh of anything – animals or themselves. Unicorn went on to explain that by eating the flesh of another animal, the memory of the way that animal lived and died was transferred into the memory of the human who ate it. By eating the flesh of the grotesque animals that were roaming the earth in the pre-crystalline days, the primitive programming was reinforced, which was just one of the many programmes that the Crystalanders needed to transform. To prevent the eating of animal flesh the Crystalanders had removed all the grotesque animals to another galaxy whose planets had a tougher terrain, more in keeping with the nature of these beasts.

The Golden Crystalanders taught humans how to choose the correct place to grow each plant, how to work with the cycles of the weather and the moon for optimum growth; how to cook the plants for food, having shown them how to use the special heating crystal they had created for that purpose.

The most important plant that they introduced to mankind was the tree. The trees were a direct connection to the Wisdom of Creation and stored within each of them was valuable information. They were the original bridges between the Earth and Crystaland. When the buds of the trees were used as remedies, it brought the physical and emotional qualities of Wisdom to whoever used them. Every plant that existed had its use, there were no weeds, there were no mistakes and there definitely was no waste. And, with the ingestion of the super water together with the plants, the physical transformation of humans started to take place. They lost the protective coarse body hair and their skeletal structure began to change, as did the structure of their brains and nervous systems. And, in time, their colouring became as diverse as the plants.

The Crystalanders taught them the technique of extracting the therapeutic qualities of plants by a process that used different parts of the plant: from the buds of trees and shrubs that gave the pure growth hormone of all plant life, to the other parts of a plant that gave specific qualities targeting different systems of the body. The specific part of the plant went through several stages of purification that ultimately produced powerful essences. These essences contained the concentrated therapeutic qualities of the plants that could then be enhanced by directing a specific intention into them thereby tailoring specific remedies for individuals. The Crystalanders had recognised the unique quality of the humans' physical body in that each person had a unique configuration of genetic coding, the difference was very subtle but it meant that their degenerative process was completely individual and each person needed a plant remedy designed to address that individual. In order to maximise the potency of the extractions, the essences were mixed with the Earth's super-water that was rich in minerals actively charged with energy from the crystal chargers. The result was a series of essences and mineral complexes that covered every aspect of a person's health from birth to death, ensuring that the

73

Wisdom of Creation would be protected and perpetuated in every cell of their body. There wasn't a condition of mind or body that couldn't be corrected should a degeneration accidentally occur.

Culinary medicine was known by everyone, so that food was used purely for nutrition and energy. The introduction of plants and remedies had a dual action: not only did they help to prevent degeneration, but they also prepared the cells of humans so that they would eventually be able to access the crystal genetic information in their bodies more readily. All these factors assisted the humans to change physically so that they eventually lost their grotesque appearance.

The more they changed physically the more the Crystalanders could help them by changing the structure of their brain and the functioning of their mind.

And, as their appearance changed, so the next stage of the transformation took place. In order for the colonisation to be successful, the transformation process needed to be accelerated and this had to be done with interbreeding. It was at this point that females had to be selected whose vibration had changed the most. The islanders had changed dramatically, and a few of them more so than others. So, from those few, twelve women were chosen to carry the pure genetic coding of the Crystalanders. They took each female and, painlessly and unobtrusively, introduced the crystal memory from the gold Crystalanders into her reproductive organs. Almost immediately each woman conceived. These women were destined to carry the pure Crystaland knowledge for eternity and their descendants would become the bloodline for the royal family of Crystal Island holding the responsibility for keeping that knowledge alive on Earth.

Orla's journey progressed and Unicorn informed her that, because the Crystalanders could not stay on

74

the Earth, they had introduced helpers who would be a constant source of assistance and information. These were little entities who became known as the faery world – elves, gnomes, and faeries. These tiny little beings, part crystal and part sound vibration, tended the plants until the humans had developed to a point where they could be taught to be gardeners and farmers. Initially the humans couldn't see the helpers but when their vibration became less dense, they were able to see these little creatures and were dazzled and mesmerised by their endeavours. Orla watched how these hard working faeries tended the plants, taking instruction from the trees, making sure that they were well spaced out, had enough soil around them and sufficient water. They later demonstrated how to harvest the crops, helping the humans to develop nurturing agricultural communities.

As the plant life grew the Crystalanders introduced bees to pollinate the ever increasing fields of plants. The bees collected the pollen to make honey to nurture and feed the queen bee and her babies. The by-product of the substance that they manufactured for the building of their hives was a substance which, when used in minute doses, was a powerful antibacterial and antiviral agent invaluable for the comparatively frail human body. The bees also taught mankind about the importance of community. The queen bee had one responsibility and that was to produce new bees. The worker bees' total focus was to provide a healthy environment for the nurturing of the next generation of bees. The structure of the hives was a magnificent example of how Crystal Wisdom translated to wonderful engineering qualities available to all inhabitants of the Earth. Each role in the bee community was of equal importance and interdependent, and the bees' work was continuous and selfless – a perfect example to mankind of the responsibility of royalty.

In Crystaland, there was no hierarchy only responsibility, which brought with it focused work and dedication. The idea of royalty was introduced to the planet to help man understand how each one of them had to take responsibility and be dedicated selflessly to the planet. Those who carried increased responsibility for sustaining the Crystal Wisdom were regarded royal.

It was at this point that Orla noticed that there were no animals. Unicorn explained that after the Crystalanders had removed the grotesque animals that had previously roamed the Earth, they had slowly introduced animals with specific qualities and purpose, but only once man had been educated not to eat flesh and had become totally satisfied with plant-based food from their newly acquired agricultural knowledge. So only a few animals were gradually introduced to help educate humans how to conduct themselves in nature. These animals were not predators or carnivores and the abundance of plant life provided sufficient food for both man and animal. Orla would eventually be introduced to these selected animals as she journeyed through the crystal paths of the Gifts and would learn how animals had lived in total harmony and equality with mankind.

Orla observed the changing landscape and the beauty of nature spilling out from the fields. As the cells of humans lost their primitive programming, they were able to be trained to see the plant-spirits. The spirit world was a naturally occurring by-product of Creation. Anything material that was created from the Wisdom of Creation had a little spirit guide. These plant spirits reflected the physical appearance of the qualities of the plants, which helped the humans understand their healing qualities. The plant spirits that helped calm the human mind were soft and feminine and moved in a languorous way. The plant spirits of the plants that had energising qualities were sharp edged, sometimes with razor shaped fins running down their back with short sharp movements. The plants that balanced female hormones were all very voluptuous and Orla smiled warmly at these rounded, glowing little beings with beatific smiles. So at first glance, the landscape appeared to be peaceful and abundant but with her newly trained sight, she could see it was teeming with the faery world and the plant spirits working together to show the humans how to work with the amazing Gifts of Wisdom.

THE GIFT OF INTELLIGENCE

Once again the path began to change colour and Orla became excited at the prospect of discovering yet another gift. She felt as if she would burst with information and marveled at the constant stream of knowledge. The crystal changed to a deep orange and the terrain around her still continued to flourish. Everything worked in harmony, the flowers were beautiful, the trees majestic, the perfumes from the plants and flowers wafting in the mild breeze of the perfect climatic conditions. Within this world of beauty, she found the coral Crystalanders with children of the humans. At this point, the humans had changed completely; their features were more refined, their posture more elegant. All had distinct individual features, differing in skin colour, hair, eyes and morphology. The children looked robust, healthy and happy and there was glee and joy within the group.

Small groups of children were with two or three Crystalanders who were showing the children how to use the powdered crystal, which they had brought from Crystaland to make articles that they needed for play. They learnt the importance of the vibrational and informational qualities of each colour. Then they learnt about shapes and experienced how, by combining certain geometric shapes with the correct colour, the result would be more powerful. Finally, they were shown how the formula combining shapes and colours was replicated in nature. With each experiment they found that when they went against the Laws of Wisdom, the article didn't have much use, or it broke quickly, whilst those articles made according to these laws lasted for generations.

Once they had mastered the concept of creating objects, they were taught the rules for using this creative process which were that all things created by man had to serve the needs of the community and the planet; objects were not for personal gain or personal amusement but instruments for assisting nature and finally and most importantly, this knowledge was a great privilege. This engaging education process held a fascination for the young and guaranteed that all young minds of each generation were introduced to Crystal Wisdom upon which the future of the planet rested.

The Crystalanders knew that the human primitive mind could only understand information in a very simple form so that it could be easily stored in their memory. So, when they taught the Gifts, the Crystalanders wore ornate vestments in the specific colour of the crystal path associated with each gift, and each vestment was decorated in the relevant geometric design. Because of the strong visual image, using colour and form, whenever they accessed these images in their memories, they would be able to release the qualities of each of the gifts into their conscious minds. These images would later come to be known as the Beautiful Motifs of Creation to be engraved deeply into the memories of future generations. It was a very simple but effective method, but only the pure of heart could access this information. If there was fear, hatred, greed or envy programmed in their memory they would not be unable to access that information.

Orla pondered on this and went back over her memory of the past journeys and in her mind was not the actual detail, just pictures of different Crystalanders projecting their different colours, but within each image was a snapshot of a whole database of information.

Orla commented on the balanced ratio of adults and children and Unicorn explained that, because the adults were living in balance and synergy with their environment, the need for conception was completely dependent on the demands of the planet. If more children needed to be born to balance the planet, then the appropriate number would be conceived. There was no mystery about childbirth. The correct number of children and their gender were born to the correct parents to perpetuate the Wisdom.

In the early days of the Crystaland colonisation, there had been many babies born in order to bring the new genetic imprint to the fore. But, before this could happen, the structure of the female form had to change to enable babies to be delivered without the possibility of the mother or baby dying.

When the Crystalanders arrived on Earth they found that young female humanoids were becoming pregnant before their bodies had a chance to fully develop. At that time the sexual motivation of the male was very primitive and without consequence. Their motivation was the propagation of the individual, a very primitive urge that they had mimicked from the wild animals and, as a result, many young girls in the first phase of puberty were impregnated before their bodies could sustain a natural birth. Another factor that made childbirth difficult was that the head of humans at that time of their development was large in relation to the size of the female pelvis, which added further complications to the delivery. Therefore, if a girl became pregnant before her skeletal structure had fully developed, this would reduce her chances of being able to deliver a healthy child.

After the introduction of the crystal knowledge and its effects on the physical structure of mankind, childbirth had become just another example of the perfection of nature and beauty. And so, with the genetic imprint from the Crystalanders, the skeleton of the human became more refined and more in balance to carry a child full term. Humans were educated not to impregnate young girls too early and females were not given partners until they were 21 so that their bodies were fully formed and strong, capable of birthing a child with no complications. When the time came for a woman to give birth there were Elders with the knowledge of crystal-midwifery, who prepared a women for childbirth by teaching her the song of birth so that by the time she was ready to deliver the child, the whole process happened in a natural, rhythmical manner. Contraception was not necessary as people were so in tune with their environment and their bodies that they didn't conceive unless their community needed more children. It was the planet that requested children to be born and not the selfish desires of individuals. Nor was it necessary for children to be born to ensure that they looked after their parents in old age. The community lovingly cared for its aging population with respect for their wisdom. With the minimisation of physical degeneration and the loving care of all sections of the community, death was not feared as it happened only after a long and productive life and each individual was content with their contribution to the planet.

It was at this stage in the development of mankind that humans were introduced to the idea that they each had a personal gift and talent. When children were growing up it was the responsibility of the Elders to identify which gift was more prominent in a child. Elders trained by the orange Crystalanders identified and interpreted to an individual what their special gift was and how it should be used for the good of the community, based on the needs of the community. There was never any challenge from an individual or the community of that decision. The Elders were able to identify the seven qualities of the intelligences from each of the Crystal worlds that were present at the time of a child's birth together with the child's lineage. The combination of those factors determined the gifts that the individual should manifest in their lifetime.

THE GIFT OF COURAGE AND LEADERSHIP

As they left the orange path, they merged onto the brick-red crystal path and once again the terrain changed. The trees were strong and tall, the plants were thick and bushy, the soil a deep brick-red, an altogether physically stronger place. The people, both male and female were also tall and strong reflecting their environment. The Crystalanders had taken the very best physical human specimens and placed them in a community to enhance their physical structure; for man to survive on Earth he would require a great deal of physical strength and agility.

Pre-Crystaland influence, the humans were no taller than four feet and, whilst they were originally created for hard work, they were easily physically overpowered by intelligence and force, and were therefore not suited for the physically and mentally challenging work that would be needed to forge communities. In order to increase their stature both physically and mentally, humans were trained with exercise, nutrition and mind control how to optimise their physical ability. With the combination of correct nutrition and the training of mind and body, coupled with the new crystal memory, the result was exceptionally strong, statuesque humans with the ability to move heavy objects with ease. However, because they embodied Crystal Wisdom they would never use their physical strength to dominate another being – or so it was hoped. The humans chosen for this role held the responsibility of protecting the Wisdom of Creation within the community. Because the early ideas of community were learnt from the animals in their immediate environment – ferocious packs with an alpha male as leader – there was an intrinsic need in humans to have leaders who they acknowledged as representing authority. These protectors therefore represented strength but in the most balanced way. Their programming from the ruby/iron Crystal world ensured that people in their charge would be treated fairly and justly with the collective objective that the Crystal Wisdom would be completely adhered to so that the planet always enjoyed abundance.

To help mankind with this concept, and because they had previously learnt so well from animals, the Crystalanders introduced the first animal to man to assist him in his understanding of the rules of nature. White Lion was chosen from a constellation, which had a solar system similar to Earth's that still followed the rules of Eternal Wisdom completely. White Lion demonstrated that supreme strength and power could also represent humility. He was a reflection of nature's strength, being finely honed to survive in nature with nothing but his physical ability, coupled with his total connection to the Wisdom of Creation. He had the physical ability to kill a human with one swipe of his paw but White Lion would never use his strength for destruction. White Lion represented the strength, perfection and responsibility of nature, and in turn respected all things that were a product of nature. White Lion's leadership responsibility was to beat his chest and insist that all beings listen to their ultimate leader, Wisdom. Man needed to know what he was dealing with – nature, like White Lion, also had two sides to her. The one side was beauty and perfection, synergy and nurturing but, if these qualities were misused or disregarded, then nature would turn her full might onto those who disrespected her with catastrophic results, as the Earth had experienced over many cycles of its history.

There was no hierarchy in Crystaland but on Earth, the humans had to have Elders to whom they could refer for guidance. The Elders in those days were women. When the Crystalanders had observed the first humanoids, they had identified that the female of the species was more receptive to the Crystaland genetic memory. The male of the species produced too many chemicals in its body as a result of the survival instinct, which rendered it more resistant to the new knowledge. Conversely, the female hormone system was compatible with the Crystaland programming, being closely connected to the universal creative process. And so it was that in time the primitive survival response was totally transformed in women but, unfortunately, only suppressed in men.

THE GIFT OF SONG AND INTUITION

Orla and Unicorn continued on the crystal path that began changing its colour, which by now she knew was an indication that she was to discover yet another Gift. The crystals on the path sparkled blue in the sunlight and as Orla scanned the surrounding terrain she saw that this experience was completely different from the others. Here there were hills and valleys, beautiful undulating landscapes with waterfalls gushing down from the mountains into swirling pools of crystal blue liquid rivers in the valleys. She observed the Crystalanders teaching the Earth children to create sound. Initially, she couldn't quite understand what was happening but on closer inspection she could see that the Crystalanders were demonstrating how sounds that the humans made echoed, and how different that echo was, depending on the environment. This was the first lesson in understanding how to communicate with the environment, which would eventually help them to fully understand the needs of the planet and indeed other humans.

The first level of understanding was to recognise the song of the Earth, they then had to recognise their own inner song that echoed their gifts. Once this was achieved, they were able to understand the emotional language – the song – of other people, making the art of communication very easy. The Gift of Song like all the other gifts would be more prominent in some humans and these individuals would be responsible for balancing the emotions of mankind. The Crystalanders recognised that the structure of human emotions was very delicate because of the early primitive programming, but they knew that there was one quality that could cut through the chaotic chatter in the minds of humans that pulled them away from Wisdom. The mechanics of the human mind was overly sensitive to outside stimuli as a result of the constant threat of danger from their original creators, which led them to be hypervigilant to that threat. So, within the Gift of Song they gave another special gift to only a few, as only a few could hold the unique connection within the structure of their minds. This special gift was the Melodies of Eternal Wisdom, the most beautiful of sounds that could erase fear and anxiety and replace it with calming stability by changing the delicate balance of man's mind. This gift would eventually become one of the most important in preserving the Crystal Wisdom in the vulnerable minds of man for eternity.

To assist them with the task of understanding the power of emotions, the Crystalanders introduced the Horse. Horses taught humans the gentle art of riding without saddle, bridle or whip but with understanding. The partnership between horse and rider could only be successful if the rider connected to the horse and 'listened' to its rhythm. Horses were naturally spirited, powerful and fast – another example of the power of Creation. If ridden without the correct connection and communication, the horse would expel the rider from its back without hesitation. Man was being taught about the force and might of the Wisdom of the universe and in so doing, was learning about the confluence of intuition, and leadership with humility. On a more practical level the horse offered man the service of carrying him further afield so that he could mix with more communities and spread the Crystaland teachings, preparing communities for their own immersion into Wisdom. And so the deeper they were able to access their own crystal memory, the more able they were to guide other people deeper into their crystal memory, with the result that mankind was capable of expressing the beauty of Creation spontaneously and be as abundant as the plant life surrounding him.

THE GIFT OF WORDS

The changing path gently faded from deep blue, losing all shade of coolness, increasing in warmth and evolved to a deep coral-orange. Orla had arrived at the place of words and she saw that when the Crystalanders arrived on Earth, man could not speak; he grunted and gestured. They were given the gift of speech that enabled them in time to learn to communicate with each other, their primitive minds excluding them from using more intelligent forms of expression.

For humans, words were an important part of the creative process as they had no other means by which to express ideas to each other, but equally they had to understand how the correct use of words was necessary for the success of the creative process. They learnt that when ugly words were used, the colours of the plants become paler, and when the words were beautiful, the intensity of the colours reflected that beauty. Negative words were never used; if people couldn't find a positive word they stayed silent; and if there was conflict or differences of opinion it was immediately taken to an Elder to resolve. They were given multiple examples of how words followed thought; thoughts had to be of pure intention and therefore words had to reflect thoughts. Absolute honesty of intention was a critical ingredient to the creative process. And, to those few who had been given the Gift of Song, they added the gift of words, which formed the lyrics for the melodies that would record the story of Crystal Wisdom for future generations.

THE GIFT OF SUPPORT

As the path ahead of Orla changed to silver, Unicorn explained to her that the first generations of crystal-humans totally understood and accepted that their role was to look after their planet. The fabric of the community was all-important; everything was shared, food, tools, words of advice, there was total openness as no individual 'owned' anything, there was joint ownership by the community. They had the understanding that they did not own the planet but that they were custodians and were so grateful to experience such light and happiness that they would never want to be any other way. Their lives were filled with daily gratitude and purity of intention. Man's experience became increasingly relaxed and happy, and as he lost his programming of fear in an environment of both strength and nurturing, the more he appreciated what the planet had to offer him. Orla had experienced this on her island but she was delighted to witness the wonderful feeling of connection that everyone on the planet was experiencing at that time.

However, mankind would need something else, something more than the help of the faery world, the animal guides and the plant spirits when the Crystalanders were gone. When they had first landed on Earth they had realised that, for them to stay for any length of time in such a dense atmosphere, they would need to recharge their inner crystal core. And so they chose four of Earth's energy centres and brought large energy crystal pillars, placing them in a circle creating an enclosed vortex. By regularly visiting these centres it would allow them to stay in the Earth's vibration long enough to complete their mission. The humans would watch the Crystalanders go into these centres, stay for a while and then come out looking bigger and brighter than ever. The humans were intrigued and fascinated by these crystal centres but when they tried to enter, the energy field was too strong and it repelled them.

The super beings knew that they would have to give mankind a way of regularly accessing and reinforcing their crystal memory in order to perpetuate Wisdom. So they built structures like their own recharging chambers but they used Earth crystals. Programmed within the crystals were all the qualities and gifts that they had brought to Earth. The Crystalanders told the humans that if they went into these crystal centres when the Earth's moon was at its fullest, they would then be able to reconnect and recharge with the original information and it would be as if the Crystalanders were still present on Earth. The human body was sensitive to the magnetic strength of the moon because of its water content, and a full moon allowed a portal to open in all of the cells of their body allowing them to be more receptive to Crystal knowledge. The Crystalanders created these energy centres for humans all over the planet wherever a community was established.

In addition to this, man also had an extra helper. Unicorn asked Orla to look closely at the humans and, as she did, she was aware of a clear cloud-like form that enveloped each person, its point of attachment being each vertebra of the spine. As with everything on the planet, the humans also had their own spirit helpers. The Crystalanders realised that each person needed a helper that was a spirit mirror image of his body and mind, an adviser to remind him of his purpose on the planet.

These beings were from another crystal dimension, they were like the spirit helpers of the plants but of course carried much more knowledge. They attached themselves gradually during the gestation period to the nervous system of the foetus, and grew with the child throughout adulthood staying with them for their physical life, communicating on an emotional level, reminding their wards of the beauty of Crystal Wisdom and how each individual was a reflection of that beauty. These spirit helpers were to be, for man, the eternal echo of the legacy of Crystaland. If an individual became confused, strayed from his gifts, the spirit helper turned his attention to the physical body of his charge and caused a pain or symptom to attract his attention as a warning that he was not acting in the best interests of his wellbeing. Humans were taught that their body was a direct reflection of their thoughts and thoughts had to reflect the beauty of Wisdom to ensure a healthy body.

THE GIFT OF BEAUTY

Unicorn watched Orla's fascination at discovering these spirit beings and she wondered about her own. Unicorn reassured her that because she had a direct lineage with Crystaland, additional helpers were not necessary and with that he gently informed her that they were nearing the end of their journey and had only two more gifts to experience. The path changed to a glittering gold crystal and very quickly, they came upon people living in communities who demonstrated unconditional love for each other without exception, which was not unusual for Orla as this was how the community of Crystal Island treated each other. She observed how they fashioned gold with superlative skill into the most beautifully crafted gifts to give each other at each of the seven Earth initiations, because the gold amplified all the qualities and intentions of the initiation. They adorned specific parts of their dwellings with gilding, understanding that the gold element was the most powerful of all the Earth's minerals as it connected and communicated to all other elements on the Earth and they wanted their dwellings to be a reflection of, and have a connection to, the beauty of Creation.

In those days gold was available to mankind in abundance as the mountains offered up its precious metal into the rivers that flowed into the communities. The mountains were rich in all minerals that were released into the rushing waters that flowed down to the rivers below. Each person loved the planet as much as he loved himself and his fellow man; there was no hierarchy – each person and everything on the planet was revered, respected and loved. And, as man's experience became increasingly relaxed and happy, losing his programming of fear in an environment of strength and nurturing, the more he appreciated what the planet had to offer him, and he was deeply grateful for that privilege. All the qualities and gifts from Crystaland had come together and mankind was flourishing and embodying the Wisdom of Creation.

THE GIFT OF UNITY

Orla and Unicorn continued through this path until it made its final change to a beautiful turquoise, whereupon the terrain changed dramatically. Either side of the path was water, amazingly clear and turquoise in colour. Unicorn explained that the Crystalanders had been attracted to Earth by the magnetic pull of the crystal soil and the crystalline water and for this part of the journey, they would have to go under the water to understand. Orla stared and enquired how long they would have to be under water because, although she was an excellent swimmer – every islander learnt to swim at a very early age – she didn't know how long she could manage to hold her breath! Unicorn reassured her that she would enter the water and she should not resist the water going into her lungs, as this water was different. There would be no interruption in her breathing; she would remember how to breathe. She looked in absolute disbelief but he explained that there was sufficient oxygen in the water for her to stay submerged indefinitely. Unicorn offered her his back to help her with the transition; she mounted him and clung nervously to his mane as he made his way towards the water.

They began their submersion into the vast body of water. As her head went under, she looked down at the back of Unicorn's head and observed in amazement how easily and happily he was walking on the fine crystal-sand. She clutched his mane frantically and was tempted to hold onto the bony protrusion on his forehead, which would have been uncomfortable for him, but she was very nervous. She was holding her breath and began to panic, then she let out all her breath, at which point she automatically took an intake of breathe and realised that she was breathing quite easily. As she relaxed into a natural rhythm of breathing, she was able to sit easily and securely on Unicorn's back.

After a while, and just as she became more comfortable with the environment, to Orla's amazement, a smiling dolphin swam up to her and explained to her that the Crystalanders had introduced him from another galaxy to teach man how to be aware of the impact of his breath in and out of water. Orla was becoming used to unexpected appearances and happenings on this most unusual journey. She was also aware that there were so many levels of understanding to this initiation and was concerned that she would not be able to assimilate all the information that was coming in so many forms. Unicorn and Dolphin smiled and reassured her that she was learning nothing new; this information was already in her memory, it was just being re-awakened. Dolphin continued narrating the story of Earth's water. By being in the water, humans gained the understanding of the interconnection of all things, the water being a wonderful illustration of that quality. When submerged, every part of a physical being was connected to the water and that interaction set off a reaction through the atoms and eventually that action was felt many miles away.

The water was teeming with highly charged atoms of minerals that joined readily in water and became powerful compounds, each one releasing a sound that communicated crystal information to other compounds. Dolphin explained that the waters of the planet in those early days of Crystal Wisdom contained the same minerals as human blood that were vital to the health of the human body and the perpetuation of the Crystaland memory. Each mineral had its own intelligence, its own sound and had its own specific role to play in every aspect of nature, in the environment, and in the human body. Without these minerals in their correct form, then the intelligence of the planet would die. As the ice that had been covering the Earth began to melt, it released the information held in the water crystals, which became the seas and the oceans, releasing and circulating information. Dolphin also told her that the remaining ice caps on the two poles of the Earth, which had been diminishing decade after decade, would reduce further. This would release more crystal information that had been locked in the ice, signaling the time for the Earth's rebirth. Orla queried this, as she was concerned that her island would be submerged in the extra water released into the oceans. Dolphin reassured her that some landmasses would disappear or diminish but Crystal Island would always be protected by virtue of the powerful energy field of the Crystal Fortress.

On dry land, the same principle occurred but it wasn't so obvious. Everything had a connecting energy field of sound – humans, plants and animals. There were always two parts to every physical entity on the planet: its physical, tangible body and the part which stored all of their history in pictorial form and was replayed in a loop over and over again, invisible to the human eye, in a space just above their head within their energy field. It was here that all information was stored of the individual with a direct connection to everyone and everything. By breathing in the air, one breathed in information and breath was the vehicle for the sound language of Crystal Wisdom. Later on, after the crystal memory had begun to recede in man, this information space would be filled with conflicting information. Stories that once told of love

92

and beauty had begun to be peppered with hatred and fear. The information that was projected from a person's energy field, determined whether they were attracted to or repelled from another. The energy fields held and transmitted the memory of the planet and therefore of man's actions, and therein lay yet another problem.

Orla noticed that there were no fish in the water just crystal formations with different levels of luminosity. After a while, a whale swam towards her. Orla gasped at the size of the whale who immediately communicated with her fluently. He told her that he was the keeper of all the Earth's memories that were stored in its waters and that the next part of the journey was to learn how the planet had evolved after the Crystalanders had left. For this part of the journey, she needed to ride on his back. She released herself from Unicorn and swam over to the whale navigating his huge body to find a comfortable place on his very broad back. Together they swam towards a large crystal structure that looked very much like an underwater gigantic crystal energy circle. On arriving at the gateway, she was stunned by its size and formation comprising more amazingly complex and beautiful geometric shapes. Whale took her through the opening with surprising ease, as she was expecting some sort of reaction from entering the structure but her body was now able to contain the difference in vibration.

As Orla dismounted Whale, he indicated to her to sit on one of the smooth rock crystals. She sat down and found herself facing an enormous flat crystal screen. Whale looked at her and realised that she was now going to undergo a brutal awakening and felt a rush of sympathy for this beautiful young women who was about to lose her innocence. For this reason he had waited for her equine companion to arrive before continuing. Whale explained that all records of mankind were held in the memory of the crystal and suggested that she make herself comfortable as this was a long and intense story. Unicorn arrived, and took up his usual place next to her. He and Whale looked at her with compassion as they knew that, although she would only be viewing a summary of the history of mankind to give her an understanding of what had happened in the world, it would be at times arduous and overwhelming and very difficult for her innocent young mind to comprehend.

CHAPTER FOUR

THE SCREENING OF THE FEAR MYTHS – OVERVIEW

On the screen the history of the planet began to unfold before Orla's intense gaze. Unicorn lay very close to her side with his head reassuringly resting gently in her lap.

Earth continued for a long while in this happy place with its band of helpers – the beings from the faery world, the plant and human spirits, and animal guides. The Crystalanders were confident that mankind now had all the ingredients to continue on its paths of transformation and were happy to leave the planet in the hands of its new Guardians. Earth's chosen Elder-leaders had been fully programmed over many generations and the overall structure of mankind's world was joyful, happy and healthy. Nature and man had learnt to live side by side in harmony, supporting, protecting and nurturing each other. The Crystalanders also knew that, if the humans continued with the regular practice of visiting the crystal circles, their programming would endure. It was time for them to leave.

The majority of mankind had settled into a very comfortable lifestyle; there was an equality that ran through all communities with an acceptance that the Crystalanders were a super-race who had given them valuable gifts for which they were eternally grateful. But eventually their primitive side began to cause conflict in a few. Without the Crystalanders protective presence, man's survival instinct was being challenged. The need to demonstrate dominance was so deeply ingrained in his programming that man became restless in this unfamiliar world of balance and abundance. That distant but familiar fear kept begging the question: *How would you survive if you didn't show dominant behaviour?*

And so the need for dominance began to creep into their consciousness again and that side in man yearned for the moment when he could rekindle the triumphant feeling that soared through his body whenever he overpowered another being.

Without the Crystalanders' presence, the humans with the more dominant primitive programming became lazy, losing the discipline to visit the crystal circles and, over time, they lost connection with their helpers and spirit guides, their crystal memory receded and their primitive side began to resent the Elder-leaders. And so the alpha male mentality slowly began to emerge – primal man sniffed the air and realised that, with the Crystalanders gone, another order could take control. The predator was waking from his slumber and he was hungry: he looked around his world searching for the weak who he knew he could dominate and control, and control he did. He had remembered that power rush of victory when committing a primal act of domination, confirmation that he had survived to live and fight another day. As the awakening began to stir in man, the planet began to emit a different vibration out into space that caught the attention of something in the deepest, darkest corner of the cosmos.

And, as time passed, something began to change. To humans, the Crystalanders appeared to be great super-beings and were seduced by their glamour, their statuesque build, sparkly appearance and supreme knowledge of all things. Humans became like children around the Crystalanders and, erroneously, man deified these super beings. The Crystalanders were not Gods, they were not the Source of Eternal Wisdom, they were purely the Guardians; the bridge between the material world and the worlds which created Wisdom, from whence all Creation came; Crystaland being a star system with seven worlds, each one embodying a quality of the Wisdom of Creation. But there was a tiny part in man that yearned to be as powerful as the Crystalanders – they coveted their glamour and hungered for what they erroneously perceived as dominance and power. This familiar desire ran through them like a quiet undercurrent just loud enough to be a constant distraction.

Over the following thousands of years, without that powerful Crystal presence, man began to forget about his Crystal discipline and, eventually he no longer aspired to be like the super-beings but directed his aspirations in a different direction. Domination birthed the concept of the 'fight for power' which became one of the first of many myths of fear that were to be etched into the memory of mankind. Orla questioned the word 'myth' and Whale stopped the screening for a moment. He smiled at the innocence of her question; someone who had only experienced the bounties of Creation could not understand the concept of the myths. Whale patiently explained to her that after humans had completed their initiation into the Gifts of Crystal Wisdom, the only reality was the perfection of those Gifts. Wisdom delivered perfection. Whenever there occurred any vestige of fear in any of its many disguises, it was purely a man-made illusion, which the Crystalanders had identified as Earth myths.

The first group to succumb to the old ways was the physically strong, those very people who had been chosen to protect and support the communities began to flex their muscles but not in a good way. These were the humans who could overpower the weak – someone who could use their physical strength to dominate until they got what they wanted. They then became jealous of the power it appeared the Elder-leaders had over communities. Jealousy was an impediment of the primitive mind; the overwhelming desire to possess the natural gift of someone else rather than accepting and focusing on the power and beauty of one's own gifts. The primitive mind could only see a two-dimensional world and therefore could only see separation. That physical separation from the Crystalanders and the recession of his crystal memory made him feel alone and unprotected, which made him doubt his very survival. That doubt drove him to possess and control that which was in his external world and he gradually lost the concept of community and unity in the face of the harsh programming of survival.

Orla shuddered as she became aware of an extra presence on the screen, which appeared as vague outline of dark shadowy figures looming by the sides of these first dissenters. Orla couldn't quite determine what or who they were but the more she focused, the more she could see their outline and then the hideous detail became more clear. Orla was seeing what was on the screen but her memory was grappling to make sense of the images as she had never in her life been exposed to such an abomination: their faces were indescribable their bodies large, bulky, dense but more worryingly she could see that they were invisible to man. They most definitely were not from any of the worlds that Orla had visited in Crystaland. These figures appeared to wait next to a human, skulking in the grey area of doubt waiting for them to stop communicating with their spirit guide.

Orla wondered what had caused the disengagement and as she continued to watch she could see that 'doubt' was the first stage of the disengagement, and where there was doubt fear would follow. When this happened the spirit guides gradually disengaged themselves from the spine of their wards as it was impossible for them to stay fully connected to people who began to doubt. And, with the increasing doubt came more fear, at which point the spirit guide would move away from the human and observe from a distance. This was not a conscious act of punishment; this was just a matter of attraction. The spirit guides only understood one language, that of love, joy and peace, but if the language changed to fear and hatred, then they automatically disengaged.

So the Shadow waited for this disengagement. Each Shadow had appendages, which were tentacles covered with jagged scales with the ability to contract, extend and entwine at will to hook deeply and securely into the memory of their prey. With the space left by the spirit guides open and unprotected in the spinal column, the tentacles of the Shadow shot out, invisibly and silently, and embedded themselves deeply into the memory of the host body. But, with limitless patience, the spirit guides never left their wards completely but stayed at a distance watching without emotion the unraveling of each human under the influence of hatred and fear, trusting that they would one day return to them and once more embrace the safety of Crystal Wisdom.

Orla was astonished at the way the Shadow was able to enter the minds and bodies of those susceptible humans without being detected and she glanced at Whale with a quizzical look on her face. He instructed her to keep observing, as all would become clear as the story unfolded. As she watched the screen she saw that the humans who had these shadowy attachments started to alter more rapidly. First their manner changed, they became aloof and cold within their community. Then their physical appearance changed, distortions of the face and body began to reflect the distortions of their mind; the beautiful lithe bodies of the physically strong becoming more dense, squat and inflexible. At that point in history the shadowy figures had become more clear to Orla, and she could see why they were embedding themselves into humans, they were feeding off them, taking all the information of the Crystal Gifts to replace it with their hatred which oozed from every scale of their ugly appendages.

As Orla watched intently, Whale explained that the Shadow had been attracted by the loneliness and fear in man that had arisen because of doubt. The existence of the Shadow was fuelled by taking the Gifts from their hosts, debasing and transforming them to hatred, stripping away all the Crystal Wisdom and leaving just raw energy which was imprinted with their unique brand of hatred. Orla could see how they attached themselves, invisibly, like parasites feeding from the neurotransmitters of the human minds and the memory portals in every cell of their bodies but the poor humans were oblivious to this energy exchange. As fear prevented humans from using their intuition, they were oblivious to the abuse that was happening to them. Orla watched with pity as more and more of this army of Shadow grew stronger in their numbers and, as their numbers increased, so the very life blood of Crystal Wisdom flowed out of the veins of mankind and was parked once again in the pages of history, waiting.

Whale reminded her that the Crystalanders had never been able to identify the cruel creators of the humanoids that they had first encountered on Earth, but these Shadow figures of hatred had been attracted back to Earth recognising that there was an abundance to feed from, even more than they had found the first time they had visited the planet. Their origins could not be identified by the purity of Crystal Wisdom, as they came from the darkest, farthest corner of infinity, a place that had ceased to be part of any of the Crystal controlled universes. This was an area that collected all the hatred of all the worlds, of all the universes, and gave it form, and Earth had become a huge magnet for that ugly and destructive emotion. And so the Shadow, attracted by the fear, attached itself to susceptible humans, gorged on their Gifts dumping hatred in their place. The hatred led to more primitive dominant behaviour, which guaranteed to instill fear deeper into the hearts of man.

As fear and hatred spread across the planet, Wisdom began to shatter and splinter and be lost. With Wisdom lost, the primal human side became more dominant and leadership was decided on the spilling of blood; the primal predator was finally awake and he had a new deity; the lust for more blood and the Cult of the Warrior began to take shape.

To ensure that Wisdom would be suppressed, the Shadow first turned on the women. The women had been selected by the Crystalanders to be Earth's Elder-Leaders because they carried the pure Crystaland knowledge. These wise nurturers could never be warriors; their physical makeup was softer and very feminine. They had not carried out physically demanding work for thousands of years and therefore stood no chance of defending themselves against men powered by hatred. And so the Shadow planted doubt, and then fear in the minds of the warriors and they turned against their Elders. Gradually the Crystal Wisdom was eroded and suppressed and

101

without the Elder-Leaders to direct, guide and remind mankind how to conduct their lives, Wisdom eventually became total suppressed.

Orla could not believe how the decision makers were the Warrior Leaders and therefore the important decisions for the future of the planet were based on primal fear. The needs of the Warrior Leaders became the priority, the needs of the community were secondary, and the needs of the planet became a voice in the wilderness. The new leaders were motivated by the desires of self-satisfaction and would therefore use the fastest route to satisfy their needs: they were beginning to mimic their predators, the Shadow. This looming darkness grew in number becoming more and more intoxicated with hatred. The primal memory together with their new programming led man to think in totally selfish terms so that the power they exercised was to dominate, rape and pillage; to take what they wanted without thought of consequences. Man needed a new formula to survive and that was to revert to the domination of the weak .

When other communities heard of these outbreaks of brutality they had to prepare to defend themselves, and so in turn chose the physically strongest in their communities to become warriors. The blueprint for war, that was to endure in the memory of man for millennia, was born. This movement spread like wildfire across the planet. The swiftness of these Warrior Leaders was aided by putting a bridle and a saddle on a horse, bending it into submission and forcing it to gallop miles and miles in a day. The horse, the sensitive animal guide that had taught man the gift of intuition and humility, had become a slave to man. By thundering across the vast plains of continents, they would catch the next community unawares; break into their gardens of tranquility, burn their homes, take their food, kill the men and force the women and children into servitude.

And whilst they were thundering across continents burning and pillaging, they had no time to cultivate food so, first they turned on their horses and used them for food, and then on the other beautiful animals who had helped teach mankind the beautiful Gifts of Wisdom. The carnivore had returned. Where once animals had taught man how to work with nature, now man taught animals the rules of survival. They too became predators and their prey was the next level down in the food chain and so the cycle continued, perpetuating the fear of the predator.

Without the wisdom of Crystaland the planet began to disintegrate, and its delicate ecosystem became out of balance. Drought and disease were rampant and uncontested. Where once stood lush fields with ripening fruits and blossoming plants now stood dust bowls. Rain had stopped coming in cyclical waves hundreds of years before. Hot countries were the first to suffer, their droughts continuing year after parched year. Each year the crops failed and the poor starved. The planet was suffering and was not regenerating so it could not offer up food because its soil had been ravaged. In the halcyon Crystaland days it rained everywhere on the planet at 4pm, just long enough to irrigate the fields and refill the rivers, seas and reservoirs. But the planetary degeneration, of course, affected the rainfall patterns. There was either a complete drought or, when it did rain, there was a deluge that would continue for weeks on end, flooding homes and the meager fields resulting in the loss of life and crops. Nature was showing the flip side of her coin and she was becoming a harsh teacher.

Worse still was when the Earth's crust rebelled against the abuse of its waters. The oceans, seas and rivers were sacred; they stored all of Creation's memories in the atoms of the minerals that flowed freely in water, giving the planet constant access to the Wisdom that was required to rebalance her. But man used the seas and waterways as vast waste disposal units filling them with detritus from chemical waste, from the many factories that made the paraphernalia of a consumer led world, and the human waste from overcrowded cities that people flocked to for employment. Most of the employment available to ordinary people revolved around the sale and manufacture of paraphernalia. Everything eventually was manufactured, even food, which led to the cessation of the traditional agricultural industry as nothing was able to grow naturally.

The landscape of the planet had become blighted by constant war and the role of the predator was constantly being contested resulting in devastating loss of life. The quest for the most lethal weaponry forced man to upgrade warfare to include a disruption in the composition of atoms, so lethal that it could wipe out whole countries with the press of a button administered from a position of safety thousands of miles away. But the only place to test these weapons was in the vast oceans, which in turn disturbed the delicate mineral balance. The seabed started to disintegrate and the Earth's crust began to shift. This caused the seas to heave in rebellion and great waves thrashed in anger against the shores of countries which devastated coastline communities in minutes.

Orla was shocked beyond words. She saw how the Warrior model had worked its way into every level of society, every culture of the world, and how the Warrior Leaders had eventually evolved into modern-day power leaders obsessed with the accrual of material wealth to the detriment of the health of the planet. She watched incredulously the picture of extreme wealth and extreme poverty. The rich stockpiling gold, money, jewels, and lavish properties whilst there were people who died for the want of fresh water. She had never seen anything so unjust in her young life and wanted to scream at the screen in front of her with outrage. There was enough for everyone, the Earth was happy to provide an abundance if it was treated with respect. But fearful, greedy people always have a paucity mentality, so their motivation is always to grasp onto power, which gives them the authority to hoard more for themselves. The power leaders made great overtures about helping the poor and the starving, but nothing was ever really done to prevent further suffering as that would have required a complete revolution of thought. Ordinary people in wealthier countries raised money through charities to try to help those suffering people, but the situation had gone past the point of no return; their efforts didn't even make a dent in the quest to prevent poverty and human suffering.

But still the people in power continued on their path of destruction. Man had taken the part of his memory that Crystalanders had given him to find solutions for problems, grafted it on to his primitive mind, which resulted in the development of more dangerous weaponry. In the early days of the warrior, the first weapons had been very primitive, one person had one hand-made weapon, but with the increase in technology and man-science they were able to develop weapons that could wipe out whole countries and, stupidly, potentially the whole planet. Without Crystal Wisdom to question whether everything that was being produced was for the planet's welfare, man-science and technology were charging full steam ahead with nothing to force it to pause and reflect. Part of the Wisdom that had been given to the female Elder-leaders was to question all actions and to reflect on whether those actions were for the global good of the planet. If the motivation for any action did not match those high standards of Wisdom, then sanction was withheld.

THE FEAR MYTH OF SLAVERY

Man was busy unwittingly creating fear-myths in his memory, none more insidious and enduring than slavery. That was the beginning of a way of life that set the standard for the future, weaving itself securely into all the history pages of mankind. It came in many guises but the idea of conquering, controlling and withdrawing freedom from another human being was fuel to the fire of power. The fear-myth of slavery of the human race was born.

The enslavement of women was probably the most heinous slavery crime of all. Man knew that, to retain power, he could not allow women to express their individuality because whenever they did, they were able to access their Crystal Wisdom which would instigate the questioning and challenging of the actions of the Warrior Leaders. To make examples of women who expressed this knowledge, they tortured, killed or enslaved them either physically or emotionally. This cycle of suppression led woman to teach their daughters to be submissive to the power leaders for fear of their girl children being punished or killed. Women were increasingly subjugated and punished for expressing spontaneity, which was the birth right of Crystal Wisdom. Religion, legends and fairy stories repeatedly depicted women as too curious for their own good and, when they followed that curiosity, it always brought themselves or others into damnation and therefore they were punished for their questioning. As women were a direct link to Wisdom; the creative force; the memory of love and harmony; man decided to contain women so that he could maintain supremacy.

However, they could not completely suppress the Wisdom as every time a woman conceived a child, she automatically reconnected to that crystal memory – no matter how distant – of the love and nurturing of Creation so that valuable knowledge could not be overwritten entirely. But men did their best by brainwashing women into believing that they were vulnerable and therefore reliant on a man for protection. They were even told at one point that they were less intelligent, their brains were smaller and they couldn't survive without a man. This lead to women developing a deep seated misogyny within themselves and instead of them glorifying in their bodies, minds and natural creative abilities they developed a self loathing with the erroneous and critical magnifying glass of man as their only term of reference. The subjugation of women became entrenched more and more into their memories and, later in history, when science-doctors took over the role of the elder-midwives who had imparted the mysteries of the creative process to every new mother, the very last fragments of the crystal knowledge was finally suppressed in women.

Man's fear of women's knowledge stretched to their being jealous of women's ability to produce children: to develop a baby inside her body and produce a perfect little miracle of creation – the ability to produce new life. Man knew on a deep level in his memory that all women carried the original genetic coding from the Crystalanders. They were jealous of that quality from which they erroneously felt excluded. In the early days there was no understanding of the physical human body and how new life was formed, so it appeared to be a miraculous achievement that a woman could spontaneously develop a child and deliver it perfectly. The ultimate feat from a survival point of view was the propagation of the species. Without the women there were no future generations. So, whilst it was important to have women, they were contained to just fulfilling certain needs of men.

Women were used as brood mares. Men lusted after women without control – a throwback to their early days of survival when sexuality was a very basic and one-dimensional instinct that was a predatory act of domination. This insidious programming, unfortunately for women, would endure for centuries. Therefore, man took his pleasure where he wanted, being able to physically overpower women. The creative sexual energy was debased to the point that it was even used as a weapon of war. To secure their supremacy, when Warrior Leaders invaded a village they impregnated the women of the village to guarantee that their fear myth programming was introduced to the next generation, thus securing their power leadership for future generations.

The Crystalanders introduced women to the many facets of creative sexuality. It was a huge project to undertake as women had become accustomed to being just physical vessels for men. Once women were initiated, they initiated men into the benefits of this aspect of Creation. Creating babies was just one small part of that whole picture. The Crystalanders also gave them the knowledge of carnal perfection and beauty so that the act of creating a child embraced and reflected the beauty of the planet and each child that was born with this programming had an innate understanding of the beauty and perfection of nature.

This powerful creative energy, when released in the correct form, reconnected with Crystal Wisdom, which rebuilt the fragile cells of the human body. Whenever man used the creative force for the basest reasons, then he reconnected to the base primitive memory of the Shadow, the Crystal memory receded and the Shadow became dominant. And so, with each child conceived in power-lust, the more the fear myths became dominant and each generation grew up more brutal than the last. The inhabitants of Earth were on a roll of destruction – of others, themselves and ultimately the planet.

Over the many centuries, Orla saw that women were forbidden to express their creative selves or their crystal intelligence. For a woman to survive she believed that she needed the protection and permission of a man – she needed a man to speak for her. Women passed from the control of their father and brothers and then to their husband. They could not own properties in their own right so therefore they could never escape from captivity. Mothers taught their daughters that to find a husband and have children was their one and only duty and, for a girl to find a husband, she had to be compliant. This meant making her husband feel strong, powerful, more intelligent than she, and his word was law. A brutal act of domination came with the mutilation of the most beautiful and vulnerable part of a woman's body that was directly connected to Crystal memory. This mutilation served to replace the beauty of Creation with brutality and pain, and led to the suppression of the creative force. So eventually, that suppression and submission further eroded the Crystaland memory, the intuition disappeared and the Wisdom was lost. The reprogramming of the predator and the suppression of women's natural creative urges was complete.

Orla was shocked to the point of trauma at this piece of history. On Crystal Island they still practiced the laws of Crystaland where women and men shared everything equally, men and women had equal authority with each person respecting the other regardless of gender. A woman could inherit title, lands and choose not to be married if she so wished; and if she did marry, she kept her family name. She was not the property of another person and was independent in her own right. But this was not the case for the rest of the planet. The women had lost their voice and eventually they didn't even realise that they had ever had a voice. They had become pale imitations of their former Crystal-selves.

Because they had lost the skill of expressing themselves confidently and assertively, tears became the only form of true emotional expression for women. Women silently wept with frustration, wept in grief for their lost memory, wept for the destruction of their planet, tears of deep sadness flowed readily from the eyes of every woman. Tears were women's only form of expressing their unconscious feelings of challenge and rebellion. Nevertheless, when a woman cried too much and too loudly, she was told that she was unbalanced and was either locked away or given chemical substances to suppress the tears. The volume of tears produced by women could have filled the oceans many times over.

Women had no authority over any aspects of their lives. In the newly industrialised workplace, young innocent girls were subjected to the sexual whims and preferences of their overseers and when they married, they were once again subjected to the whims and demands of their husbands. And when the children come along in quick succession, they had no authority over their precious children's welfare, no influence over how they were conditioned, allowing the perpetuation of that fear-based programming to continue unabated throughout society.

Eventually women fought hard and suffered terrible privations for more authority over their lives and were eventually given the right to vote in the elections of governments – the first step in a very long and difficult journey that gave women the opportunity to influence what happened in their lives. Eventually they were allowed a degree of authority over the welfare of their children, but this degree of freedom was heavily suppressed by the threat of physical or mental violence from their husbands. Domestic violence was not governed by the law of the land, granting carte blanche to any husband who wished to silence his wife with menace. An important factor which eventually gave women more authority over the bodies and their lives was the ability to control when they became pregnant. Before this, women were pregnant every year of their fertile lives and, as a result, often died young. During those years, there was no time for a woman to express herself: she was worn out, reflecting the exhaustion of the planet.

There were two great wars in the 20th century where women worked in factories carrying out the work that had previously been the domain of men. This started to break the spell of limit and constraint. In the latter part of the 20th century, women were educated and were given more senior roles in industry, but still they had deep in their memory the programming of being punished for expressing their intelligence, which created inner conflict and confusion. Whenever a woman was confronted by a man expressing the power-leader energy, there would be a ripple of fear echo through her survival memory, silently and insidiously catapulting her emotional response to a memory of the actions of the Warrior Leaders, which prompted her to question herself to a lesser or greater degree. This hesitation prevented her from being spontaneous – the very quality that accessed Wisdom. It was as if women were waking up gradually from a long sleep. The problem was that sleep was peppered with nightmares detailing memories of suppression, slavery and debasement at the hands of their captors, the power leaders.

With more women in the workplace without true role models of female authority, they tried to act like the power leaders, which led to internal conflict, an imbalance in their physical and mental health and a confusion and mistrust amongst the men. Nor was it easy for women to work in industry whilst being mothers. At one period in history women were encouraged to work full time, run a home and bring up children; working right up to the time of birth and then going back to work when the babies were months old. They had been sold the myth that 'they could have it all' and therefore could do it all. So, although women were better educated and were doing the same jobs as men, they were mentally and physically exhausted. They were trying to do two jobs and one of them, which was the nurturing of the future generation, being the most important job for the future of the planet. They were being pulled in so many directions that they were physically not functioning well at all, leading to the disruption of the female hormones which pushed their Crystal memory further and further into the recesses of their minds. Women were mirroring how humanity was treating the planet but neither the planet nor women were designed to function this way. The structure of the workplace was a direct replica of the blueprint of the war model, which caused conflict and discord in the memory of women. Women were achieving nothing; they were too exhausted, over stimulated and distracted to make the valuable contribution to society for which they were destined. These were the individuals whose crystal programming could have allowed them to question the power leaders, question the structure of society to harness and direct the full throttle of mankind – if they could but only access their full Crystal programming.

THE FEAR MYTH OF ADDICTION

One of the many tragedies to blight mankind was the destructive force of addiction. Man thought that he was a strong warrior and that was the way to express power. But, they still had the crystal memory deep in their understanding and whilst it was not as dominant as it was in women, they still had a sense of abundance and joy trapped within their deep memory. There was no real joy to be found naturally in their daily lives – separation and loneliness was a feeling that was always lurking on the perimeter of their emotions. Therefore they needed to find something to silence that need to reconnect to Crystal Wisdom. The warriors in battle elevated the fear-chemicals in their body to such a high degree to give them false courage but when the fear chemicals wore off they needed something to give them a sense of peace, quickly – this substance was called alcohol.

Orla watched as addiction started to seed itself into the minds of man. Addiction was the condition that always attracted the attention of Shadow. When man was under the influence of a substance, he was at his most vulnerable. All his crystal barriers receded deeper into the darkness of his memory as the language of the intoxicated mind was alien to Wisdom. This retreat left a gap, a vulnerable space in his emotional memory and that was all it would take for the Shadow to sink its tentacles of hatred into an individual's memory and another meal ticket had been recruited.

However, whilst man was plundering, pillaging and generally being brutish, there was a side to him that was crying out for expression. The more he exercised his primitive side the more the crystal side of his memory constantly tapped on the walls that imprisoned that beautiful Wisdom. This created disquiet in his being, a feeling of loneliness and separation, and there was always an underlying depression whenever they came back from a battle. The addiction to alcohol was the first in a long line of addictions that was to both control and destroy the most brilliant minds of men. There would always be that inner yearning, something missing, no matter how many battles they had won, how much gold they collected, there would still be an inner searching to fill a gaping hole in their emotions. This deep yearning was not satisfied by the material conquests of war. The part of their memory that was buried and had become calcified was still pulsing quietly at a profoundly deep level having retreated from the Shadow's tentacles. The only way to silence the constant inner nagging of the missing piece of the puzzle of their emotions, the feeling of isolation, disconnection and sadness, was to use alcohol to fill that gap. It did the trick, never failed, but the effects only lasted a short while. When those effects wore off the deep yearnings would come back even stronger causing conflict, doubt and guilt, which was often so strong that they needed more and more alcohol to squash those excruciatingly uncomfortable distracting emotions.

The distillation and fermentation process was given to humans to help them make the optimum use of their plants, using alcohol to release the therapeutic qualities from plants. However, greed was a component of the Warrior Leaders and the distillation produced from some of the grains gave these men such a kick of heat and energy that they used it more and more, which in turn affected their brain chemistry, calcified the crystal memory, increasingly releasing the primitive memory. Then they realised that the kick they got from the alcohol not only helped them celebrate their warrior successes by lifting them into a state of euphoria, but helped them to fight stronger, harder and longer in battle. So, the Warrior Leaders gave their troops alcohol before a battle to ignite their passion and encourage them to fight fearlessly. Even after man had become more sophisticated with his warmongering, using weaponry rather than foot soldiers, the 'fearless warrior' programming continued to be prominent in the memory of man and was easily triggered. When men and women drank too much alcohol in their increasing quest to recapture that feeling of Crystal joy and peace, their minds would play tricks on them releasing the 'fearless warrior' memory and the result was inappropriately aggressive behaviour towards each other. Examples of this were seen in every town and city of the world. The landscape of the high streets of relatively sophisticated communities changed after dark, young people would fight each other in blind aggression and the streets became primitive tribal war zones. Amazingly, alcohol was sold freely to the public even after it had been proven to ruin the minds and bodies of man. But alcohol was yet another way of controlling the masses, by keeping them slightly out of control on a regular basis, it kept them in an unconscious state during their sober hours. Humans under the influence of any addiction did not have their eyes on the ball. They were either under the influence of the addiction or in a state of recovery. The effects of taking these substances ranged from the destruction of their brain chemistry, to the poisoning of their body's organs. Both conditions prevented humans from questioning and challenging. Their focus was inward rather than outward looking, isolating them further from the reality of their situation. Their addictions were varied and many – sugar, alcohol, tobacco, and many other substances, both legal and illegal.

The honeybee, who had been introduced to the planet to show man how to work with nature, was another victim of this epic tragedy. When the faery world had retreated because of the inhospitable environment of Earth, it had fallen solely to the honeybee to pollinate the plants. But man had tasted the honey, and recognised that he got a quick fix from its sugar content, he also discovered the wonderful alcoholic drink that it made. The problem was that the honey nurtured the next generation of bees; without sufficient honey, the young bees did not survive which led to dire consequences for the plant life of the planet. So man set up colonies of bees where daily the hives were 'milked' for their honey. The little enslaved worker bees were exhausted trying to keep up with demand, and when the plant life began to diminish because of the planet's degeneration, the bees had to travel further afield to find plants to collect the pollen, adding to their exhaustion. At that time, man's thirst for honey was rising as it was regarded as a 'healthy' sugar – one of the new addictions. The human body did not need sugar but a whole industry had evolved based on products made from it – another addiction that would lead to never ending physical and mental health problems. The addiction to sugar would eventually become a major contribution to man's physical undoing.

At that point, Whale realised that Orla was stunned by the cruelty of the information that she had witnessed and he drew her away from the viewing chamber. Her innocence had been broken and he could see she was grappling with the amount of pain that had been inflicted across the planet over the centuries. Unicorn realised that it was almost too much for her to absorb in one sitting and gently nuzzled her arm, as he felt so protective towards his young innocent charge. But she had to undergo this crash course in man's destruction of the planet and it had to be conducted in stages as she needed to rest in between. Whale considered his little student and realised that what she was viewing was a sanitised version of the fear myths. Had she been shown the full extent of the depravity that existed on Earth, she would have been completely traumatised. Whale knew that she had been given sufficient information for her level of comprehension at that time. When she returned to Crystal Island, she would be older and would eventually discover the full extent of Earth's cruel destruction.

Orla was a little confused with the idea of addictions and asked Whale why humans were so vulnerable to certain substances. Whale explained that, such was the strength of the crystal memory, although it had retreated to the deepest recesses of the human mind, it could never be totally eradicated and this memory was an eternal echo in the cells of every human of the beautiful Wisdom of Creation and that echo caused a deep grieving for its loss. During the Crystaland civilisation humans had been consciously connected to pure Crystal Wisdom at all times filling their emotions with abundance. So it became a constant quest to satiate that thirst, an eternal longing for that Crystal connection. Certain substances accessed that echo of crystal joy, but it was just an echo not the real thing so it only lasted for a short while. Each time they accessed the echo, the echo retreated deeper into the memory not wanting to be exposed to the chaos and so more of the substances had to be taken to chase the echo. Addictions could only provide a temporary bridge to a paler version of that real connection.

Orla had been equally perplexed at how the slavery programme became deeply imbedded in every day life. She had seen how more and more people became enslaved by the Warrior Leaders. "How could this be?", she asked her mentors "Each and every individual is special and deserves respect and freedom". Unicorn, unfazed by her naivety, explained to her that the Warrior Leaders were lazy; without the security of Crystal Wisdom, they were becoming seduced by their addictions to replace that security – with addictions to alcohol, the pleasures of the flesh, food, gold and most of all to power.

Whale suggested that Orla rested before seeing the next chapter of life on Earth and led her outside of the viewing chamber. She lay down next to Unicorn and promptly fell asleep. Her dreams were full of her experiences in the different worlds of Crystaland, they invigorated her, and when she awoke she was ready for the next session. Whale took her back into the viewing chamber knowing that the next viewing would be particularly hard for her to absorb.

THE FEAR MYTH OF THE SUPPRESSION OF FREEDOM

Orla sat eagerly in front of the screen and before her eyes another theme of history began. This time it was focusing on the way man treated the children of the planet – the most important asset that Creation had, the future Guardians. After the Warrior Leaders took control of the planet, the knowledge of plants for healing also gradually diminished and left humans vulnerable. In those early warrior days, many of the children did not reach their first birthday, so many babies were conceived to restock the constant outpouring of death – death by ignorance and death from battle. The children who survived birth and their early years were those who were physically stronger – strong carriers of the fear myths.The conquering warriors always took slaves from the communities that they invaded and captured, and used them as beasts of burden. The programming from the original humanoids was truly coming to the fore with a vengeance. Their lives were short but there were always many more slaves to take their place. The warriors then thought it would be prudent to breed from the slaves so that there would be a constant supply, removing the need to laboriously transport them when captured from war zones. And so, to these wretched humans little lives were born, born into slavery with no understanding of freedom, with no experience or knowledge of the ability to run and play in the sun. They were tethered from birth to death to a life of misery and servitude, which would eventually become the blueprint for the work ethic for the majority of the human race. The tragedy was that they looked on at the lifestyle of their owners, the Warrior Leaders, saw that they had lives of privilege, comfort, excess and freedom, and with time accepted that their role in life was just to serve, feeling that they deserved no better. They had totally lost any sense of self-worth and accepted that there was a hierarchy in life, a two-tier system whereby there were the privileged and non-privileged, which it would appear could never be changed. Society's cruel hierarchy of fear was burned at that moment into the hearts and minds of humanity.

At this point, it was Orla who was weeping. This was a girl who had known few tears in her life. The only time that she had shed a tear was when she had fallen and hurt herself when she was very little or when one of her beloved animals had come to the end of its Earth life. But these were the tears of deep sadness and a grieving for the ugliness of mankind had how the inhabitants of Earth were devouring their home. She also couldn't comprehend the fear that men had of women. On Crystal Island, it was common knowledge that the females were the carriers of crystal knowledge, but that equally all men inherited that knowledge and they were happy to be a part of its continuum. There was complete mutual respect between men and women. Each person on the island knew the power base was not of human origin – it belonged to the planet. This was an island that was a nature-led society – not a society led by primitive needs and desires.

The theme of slavery continued throughout history in both an overt and covert way. As time continued, there was a muttering of rebellion – a few enlightened people who fought for the abolition of slavery. The law was changed but it was too late: the blueprint of slavery was well and truly tattooed onto everyone's memory.

Slavery continued, therefore, but in different guises. Everyone appeared to be free but, and here was the big 'but', to survive in a hedonistic material world you had to work for the Warrior Leaders. The warriors no longer wore suits of armour, proudly displaying their battle scars. No, these warriors had fashioned themselves to be educated, wise and liberal leaders. They might have looked like caring human beings but this was a façade. The only way they could have been truly caring and wise was to have had dominant Crystal memory evidenced by the priority of caring for the planet. This was obviously not happening because the model they were using to rule people was still based on the fear myths. Where there is fear there is no Wisdom and no Creativity. Moreover, ironically, the aspirations of the common man were not to be free but to be chained to their material lifestyle; their role models were the new power leaders, their captors.

As time went on and the need for the paraphernalia of materialism became more urgent, early industrialisation introduced an ugly form of slavery. The innocent children became labourers alongside their parents, engaged in the harsh life of survival. There were only a few people who had comfortable lives, the rest were nothing more than slaves. And so the suppression of the freedom of childhood continued, children being born and dying from disease or privation before maturing. If they survived those brutal first years, they were sent to work at the age of five or six in inhumane conditions. Orla had tears rolling down her face again as she saw the tragedy of the daily toll on their lives – no light, no play, no nurturing nor any qualities required for healthy development – physically and emotionally.

THE FEAR MYTH OF EDUCATION

Then came the books. By this time man had decided what was right and wrong in terms of the power base and had created a way of judging based on the formulation of words which they called logic and reason. This ensured that the words made sense but the Truth of Wisdom was sometimes obscure. But it was this very process which led to what was called science, medicine and law, the three major authorities that eventually would decide the fate of mankind. This process would ultimately lead man to believe, erroneously, that he knew as much, if not more, than Creation. The use of words had been dumbed down to a two dimensional formula that excluded the Crystal word formulas reflecting the sound of creation and therefore illuminating the Truth. The teaching of Crystal Wisdom was an oral tradition and never written down, for it was the vibration of the spoken or sung words that connected man directly to that Wisdom.

Eventually some enlightened people helped change the laws to prevent children from being exploited in industry to enable them to have a better education. So the children were removed from the oppression of the factories and the mines but were forced to spend hours every day in a classroom with a teacher dictating to them facts, logic and reason – another form of enslavement. The creative side of these children was being closed down. Spontaneity, one of the closest links to the Crystal memory, a gift to all mankind, was suppressed at a very early age and therefore the desire to question was literally ironed out of their vocabulary. To the boredom, they added the stress of intense examinations, introducing collective competition and a pass or fail mentality. The fear subtext of that mentality was to survive or not. Children had to regularly take exams from a very early age, upon which they would be judged and assessed as to their potential, the results of which would stay with them, good or bad with all of the inherent limitations, for the rest of their lives. So much fear was being programmed into young people that they had to suppress their natural urges of expression, and when that happened their minds did not work correctly and they became vulnerable to the slightest substances that might release them from their inner prison...what was that, ah yes, the addictive substances.

Humans had inherited from the Crystaland memory a condition of the mind, which, if uncontested by survival fear, allowed them to produce feelings of unbridled joy and happiness. This was the default mode of every child, inherited at conception, unless of course they were put into primal fear-induced situations of oppression. They then became vulnerable to substances like alcohol, tobacco, chemical stimulants, and plant hallucinogens to name but a few. The most sensitive of children, those who had dominant Crystaland memory were the little individuals to feel the most distress. They could not make sense of the world into which they had been born. What they were experiencing was in direct conflict with their deep memory, which stored echoes of happy times, balanced times, times of peace and joy. These were the very people who could have helped turn the tide of their degeneration. Within them was a deep ache, a longing, and when they touched any of those substances that gave a quick fix, a hit of pleasure, it transported them temporarily to that joyful place for a small moment in time and they wanted to stay there because it made them feel like they had come home. These sensitive ones then became addicted to the substances because the world around them was too painful to endure without the relief of the momentary euphoria that their addictions provided. Many of these sensitives had carried the Gift of Music, which is a direct connection to the song of the universe, and within them, they yearned to reconnect to that song and express that song in its many forms to the people and everything else on Earth.

But the cacophony of the material world and all its incumbent fears drowned out that song and they felt lost and hollow, their creativity lost in a sea of meaningless noise being generated by the power leaders who had identified music as another medium to control and also to make money. Whale glanced at Orla as she sat attentively watching the screen trying to make sense of the chaos before her. He reminded Orla that sound, in all its colours and shades, which includes words expressed within the Truth of Wisdom, would be the only quality to bring the Crystal memory back into the consciousness of mankind. Orla thought about this deeply and reflected on her journey through the Sapphire and Silver Crystal world and the music on Crystal Island. The music was beautiful and captivating, reflecting the many facets of Creation through the instruments, which had been perfected for centuries to reflect accurately the melody of the Earth. The string instruments were more evident as they captured the undulations of the emotions of the different landscape beautifully and the accompanying lyrics described the many and various stories of Crystal Wisdom. Orla's musical strength was in writing powerful lyrics and matching the lyrics with corresponding melodies, oh how she loved doing this. This was a gift that she would develop even further when she returned to Crystal Island. Both her parents played musical instruments creatively and she reflected on her father's wonderful voice that embraced and expressed strength and power, which had the ability to create balance out of chaos.

THE FEAR MYTH OF
SLAVERY IN INDUSTRY

The Warrior Leaders had hungered for more and more ways to gain and retain power and had introduced the idea of money and trade. Instead of each community providing for everyone in its community, the community had to provide for the Warrior Leaders. In the early days, it started with bartering and then it became more sophisticated. Recognising the value in the precious mineral gold, gold coin was used to represent power. The more gold coin you had, the more powerful you were. And, when the planet eventually stopped offering up its gold in the streams that flowed from the mountains, the leaders put the slaves to work underground to dig the gold out of the Earth. The raping of nature's resources was widespread both above and below ground.

With the eventual abolition of slavery, people were paid for their work but they had to work so hard for little rewards that the fear programming was still being perpetuated. What was different from the days of official slavery? Over the centuries the theme of slavery became even more sinister. The power leaders had been forced by various legislation to pay their workers more. But, that cunning primitive brain saw an opportunity to turn this to its advantage. The working people were seduced into spending their money on paraphernalia or services that they did not really need but were manufactured by the power leaders. There was such an outpouring of spending by workers that vast amounts of profits were made by those power leaders. The money that they paid to their workers eventually made its way back into the bulging coffers of the power leaders – so clever. With so much materialism, the need to work more and more became a fear motivation. Fear stalked workers waking lives, haunted their dreams, and disrupted their sleep. Fear transformed into worry; worry about keeping jobs and not being able to continue to buy all the unnecessary 'things and stuff' and 'services' that they had been conditioned to believe were vital to a successful life, and indeed, to their survival.

Orla looked on at the array of objects that these people thought were essential to life: vehicles in all colours and sizes which used up vast amounts of fuel from the ever decreasing supplies of the planet; houses and items for the house that needed to be replaced regularly as a newer and shinier version appeared on the shelves. In addition to polluting the minds of mankind, the manufacture of all these unnecessary articles also polluted the air and the waterways and depleted the vital minerals from the earth.

Such was the brainwashing that man's main goal in life was to earn more gold from his job, and those who earned the most were regarded as having reached the pinnacle of success. Those who accumulated immense wealth replaced the Warrior Leaders and became the power leaders safe in the knowledge that, whilst there was fear there would be no questioning, no enquiry, no challenge. The warrior roared and beat his chest in triumph.

The perplexed Orla asked Whale why the Crystalanders had not come back to the Earth and reversed the spiral of degeneration. Whale explained that there were two important factors that allowed Crystalanders to be able to enter Earth's atmosphere. One was that the vibration of the planet, which had changed beyond all recognition, had become very dense – too dense for them to survive. When the Crystalanders had come to Earth originally the fibre of the planet was still functioning, it had just not been developed. That fibre had been destroyed and the Crystalanders would not have survived in the polluted environment of Earth. Another important factor was the Shadow. The Shadow, whilst being attracted to man's primitive fear, had contributed largely to humanity's vibration becoming so dense that he would not have been able to recognise the Crystalanders. To be able to see their form, man had to be innocent; the Shadow had taken man's innocence and replaced it with corruption. Whilst man had been very primitive when the Crystalanders first appeared, he was relatively innocent: he had no other knowledge. Man now had taken knowledge and had manipulated it to suit himself to make his own rules. All the Crystalanders could do was to scan the events from the safe distance of other galaxies and observe the degeneration.

They had seen this many times before with planets in other universes, each time it happened it ended with an almighty apocalypse. But this time there was hope, this time the people from Crystal Island had kept the pure Crystal memory dominant for thousands of years and it was still active. The Crystalanders watched and waited to see if this time man would wake up to what he was doing to his home, banish the squatters and elect to be a better tenant. Whale explained that throughout history, there had been people who had tried to reverse the philosophy and practice of degeneration and they had been called holy men and prophets. These pioneering men had been able to see the Shadow and therefore recognise the ugliness that had crept into mankind. This had worked for a while; people were listening and were being drawn back to seeking the Crystal ways but the power leaders saw this as another opportunity to control the masses. So they infiltrated the new organisations of the new philosophies, distorted the message and installed a warrior-hierarchy into their administration. The Cult of the Warrior inhibited the message of compassion and mercy and replaced it with a strict dogma that filled the vulnerable with guilt instead of mercy, making them easy prey for the manipulation of the power leaders. The words of compassion and mercy, as taught by the holy men, were suffocated in a sea of false piety. Eventually the bitter veneer of this dogma was exposed in scandal and the people became disillusioned, turning their back on the teachings of those 'holy' people.

But this message resurrected that longing inside them; it interrupted the fear myths momentarily and, in their desperation, they turned to anyone who seemed to have a new philosophy whether they were authentic or not. This was the period of the false prophets and gurus. Mankind was still looking for that part of himself that represented Wisdom and it appeared that anyone who spoke of 'enlightenment', 'spirituality' or 'self empowerment' was erroneously and dangerously elevated to Mastery. The worship of deity was programming that had evolved after the Crystalanders had left. It was man's constant search for that higher part of himself but, instead of looking for it within, he chose to look outside and he was easily duped. And, because man had forgotten what authentic Crystal Wisdom was, he accepted any poor imitation. Once again, he was open to manipulation by his predators.

Whale explained to Orla that there had been many people who had warned that misuse of the planet's natural resources would be a major cause for the degeneration of the planet, but they had been only partially correct. He went on to explain that the most dangerous toxin was the thought-forms created by their fears, which in turn attracted more Shadow. Orla reflected on her journey through the different worlds of Crystaland where she had witnessed the powerful results of pure intention and focus. Whale explained that fear intensified the malignancy of the intention and rendered it more destructive. The biggest danger to the future of planet Earth was the intention of hatred for each other – in all its colours and shades – that was carved into every memory cell of mankind.

Orla shook her head in disbelief and her attention

shifted wearily back to the screen. She could now see, by using her newly acquired ability to scan the energy levels of all things, that not only were the humans more dense, but also the air around them was dense. The vibration of the atoms had slowed down which meant that the regenerative process was too slow. In nature, there is always a breaking down and building up, that is the cycle of life, but the breaking down process was overtaking the building. The Shadow was taking creative energy and giving only hatred back. Where there is hatred there can be no creativity only destruction. The new philosophy of man was to overpower, take, and destroy. Orla could see the detrimental effects of the collective fear-energy all over the planet. She was witnessing how the most destructive force to the planet was coming, not from the physical atrocities, but from the thoughts and words of mankind.

Over time, the manufacture of 'things and stuff' and the accrual and storage of gold had become super-sophisticated. The new science called technology took on a life of its own and created a completely new industry. Orla watched how it had rapidly seduced the masses. However, she could see its value. Mankind was only using a minute amount of his brain capacity so he needed lots of aids to help him remember data. Society had become so complex that detailed records had to be kept of every facet of a person's life. But, what thrilled her most about this industry was that it began to give people access to their own creative process. On Crystal Island, they were able to access within their own memory any configuration of creativity, and produce wonderful examples of that expression. Poor mankind had lost those skills but was rediscovering the possibilities. But, instead of assisting man, technology was taking over – or so it would appear.

Scarily, the business world – the world of the manufacturers of paraphernalia and the provision of services – had made huge mistakes repeatedly and Orla looked on incredulously at how they had refused to learn from those mistakes. She amusingly thought that the repetition of the same action that did not work must be a sign of stupidity or insanity. Whale explained to her that trading had mushroomed from the small cooperatives to massive international organisations and the only tools these poor people had who were responsible for these large organisations, were the tools of the fear myths of the primal warrior leaders. Nothing had changed in this formula. Technology had developed in quantum leaps but man was still running his life according to the formula of primitive man. There were rumblings of the need to do things differently and finding creative solutions to business problems became the Holy Grail. This resulted in a plethora of personal development training courses, coaches and mentors trying to help the business leaders change. Systems were formulated which purported to be able to define, measure and categorise the potential of an individual to identify the best candidates for creative leadership. But, once again, this model was flawed. The dogma of these systems was that an individual had to fall into limited groups or categories, upon which their potential was identified and labelled, leading to them being limited and defined within the very narrow parameters of what was in effect the primal fear programming. The tragedy was that those people who were conducting the measuring and labelling exercises were not coming from a place of Crystal Wisdom but from the warrior memory and, although advice was given, it was invariably the same answer to the same problem but packaged differently to make it look new and innovative. True creativity only comes from an unfettered mind, unfettered from the conditioning of warrior/power-led industrialisation. The blind were leading the blind so that the results would invariably be the same. Where there was fear programming there could be no Wisdom, intuition or creativity. Decade after decade the same mistakes were made, and each time there was a failure, failure became more deeply programmed into man's memory. Failure was etching itself deeper and deeper into the collective memory, which in turn gave rise to more fear.

THE FEAR MYTH OF DISEASE

After the Crystalanders left Earth and the Warrior Leaders took over completely, it took man many hundreds of years to try to understand the workings of the body. During those days of Crystaland perfection, good health was taken for granted and a detailed understanding of physiology was not required. When the super-beings left the planet and, just at the point where the new science and the old ways could have made a perfect union, the introduction of chemical medicines became the gold standard. Once again, man had not fully understood the complete picture; he had half a story and was running with it. Disease was regarded as something that needed to be stopped and suppressed. Over the years, because of the imbalance in nature, the bacterial makeup of the Earth became dysfunctional which created an environment whereby disease erupted more and more in the bodies of mankind. Disease was Earth's way of waving a red flag to humans as a sign that they were abusing themselves and their planet and that abuse was reflected and manifested in their health. The men of science, however, decided that it was more cost effective to manufacture chemicals rather than use plants to fight disease – man was at war again. What they were not aware of was that disease – like man – had strong survival programming. The viruses were a product of nature and were cleverer than science so they mutated, played dead, changed shape and became a different disease. Therefore, whilst one disease was suppressed, it popped up as another disease later. And so it continued, with the final result that nothing could be manufactured by the chemical industries that could fight the strong, resistant diseases – disease became humanity's new predator. The constitution and immune system of mankind had been downgraded; man began to lose his vitality, was reduced to a shadow of his Crystal self and was vulnerable in the face of the ever-increasing diseases.

This was something that money could not put right. Power leaders were affected just as much as the poor. The difference was that the poor died faster. The power leaders just kept finding a new chemical to kill one disease and then when another disease appeared, they threw money into more research, found a new 'miracle cure', made more money, and so the cycle continued chasing the same dragon's tail. Small groups of people who had tried to resurrect the old ways of healing tried to reintroduce a pale version of Crystaland ways but there were flaws here. Their memories were sketchy. The fear programming embossed into their memories, stronger with each generation, had stopped them from accessing the Crystal Wisdom from which new answers could be found. They knew that plant remedies were used in the old days but those ancient healing plant remedies did not work so well in the modern world. When the Crystalanders introduced those plants to the Earth, the soil and the waters were teeming with minerals that nurtured the growth of super nutritious plant life. The whole structure of the planet nurtured these plants and, when the essence of the plants were extracted, powerful remedies were created that were highly effective on the human organism. The problem occurred when they tried to use plants that were grown on depleted soil and therefore lacked the active ingredients. Equally, the human body had become so toxic that the energy of the plant remedies was too feeble to enter the cells of the body. The water used to extract the essence was dead water. In the early days, it was the mineral rich water that had been energised by the crystals of Crystaland that increased the strength of the plant extracts. The crystal formations, which had once dotted the energy points on the planet, were as dead as the soil. The crystals had turned to solid rock. The soil was now dust; no fragment of crystal remained.

But here too the power leaders tried to take control of the healing power of nature. They endeavoured to replicate the plant remedies by replacing the active ingredients of plants with artificial chemicals. They recognised that mankind was waking up to the understanding that different solutions had to be found for health and saw an opportunity to control another industry and therefore the spending power of mankind. At that point in history, the pharmaceutical industry was the biggest and only growth industry on the planet. It even outranked the sophisticated weapons industry. But, whilst they were able to identify the active ingredients of plants and chemically replicate them, what they couldn't do was to replicate the creative value of the plant. The creative value was the part of the plant that held together all the active ingredients and acted as a catalyst to their synergistic action. Without that, the remedy was ineffective. The degenerative process had a good foothold on mankind. All those ancient remedies which had been created to aid regeneration were destroyed by the programming of greed and the concept of preventative medicine was totally overwritten by fear. The invaluable knowledge of the benefits of how plants and minerals help to repair and build the immune system was lost and, because the fear programme had damaged their crystal memory so much, humans were unable to access that powerful and liberating knowledge.

By the 21st century, the number one disease of mankind was a sadness so profound that it was given the name depression. Whilst the physical body was degenerating, it was also having a deep effect on the mechanism of the emotions. With the constant overlaying programming of fear, the mind became exhausted. Many chemicals were manufactured to try to mimic the brain chemistry to produce joy but scientists were just looking at the physiology of the brain and not the energetic factors of the whole body. So with depression came the drugged state – not the obvious drugged state but a more insidious condition. Worryingly, more and more people were given cocktails of chemicals to help their depression. But if the chemicals were effective – often they were not – then the individuals who took them looked as if they were functioning normally but their minds were not. They lived on a plateau of bland. No deep lows and no deep highs, just bland. And where there is bland, there is no spontaneity. Where there is no spontaneity there is no creativity, questioning, and no challenge. The power leader still did not understand; his arrogance was again preventing him from seeing deeply. The human condition was more than just a physical body that could be measured, weighed and tested. There was an aspect of humans that had its own intelligence – each individual had the ability to know inextricably what was right for him or her – deep in memory was the crystal intelligence which they could link to once their fear programming was cleared. This intelligence could never be measured by man-science, which is why man-science would never fully understand the working of his memory. In the meantime the experiments continued with chemicals and 'therapies' but this was a dangerous game. There was no understanding of the depth of vulnerability or the sanctity of the inner workings of mankind's memory. Those subtleties were only to be found through Crystal Wisdom.

Orla had virtually stopped breathing and had a look of disbelief and shock on her face. She had gone past the stage of tears. A deep shock and a rising feeling that she had never felt before replaced the tears. This was a feeling of outrage. This was the very feeling she needed to help her understand what was required for her future role. Her maternal side was outraged, her paternal side was outraged, every part of her was outraged at how mankind had distorted itself and how wicked and cruel it had become. She felt a deep thrust of energy urging her to wipe out this outrage, this insult to Creation from the face of the Earth. Whale and Unicorn observed her reaction and were pleased, her initiation was activated. Here was the first new crystal warrior, the first of many who would bring the Earth back to the obedience of Creation. Orla was impatient to move on and come to the end of this horror story and the screen filled with the dark history one more time.

THE FEAR MYTH OF FOOD PRODUCTION

During this session Orla would learn about the travesty of food production. The agricultural industry survived in a natural way for many hundreds of years but eventually there became a need – which was an artificial need – for the quick fix of feeding, as the farming of animals became a high production industry. To fulfil the need for animal protein' cattle were used for milk production and were housed in metal barns closely packed together, never seeing the sunlight or fresh grass, where they stood all day being milked by machines. Chemicals were given to the cows to increase milk production but the quality of the milk was poor. In addition to the poor nutritional value, the same chemicals that were given to the cows to increase production were passed through their milk to humans who drank it which caused serious health problems. New developments in science brought the cloning of animals in an attempt to find a solution to the ever increasing demand for food. But the scientists didn't understand the creative intelligence that is the matrix of all life and just as they had failed to replicate effective plant remedies, they created animals with severe genetic problems which resulted in them becoming even weaker than their natural predecessors.

The animals left for food production were fed rubbish and pumped with chemicals to counteract the effects of over-production, disease and cheap feeding plans. The meat from animals was so low in vitality it could not be used for man or beast. Milk production stopped completely and was replaced with a milk substitute, which was just chemicals. People were eating and drinking empty calories; food with no nutritional value that made them eat even more – they were never satisfied. Throw in the sugar and alcohol consumption and the results were people who were unhealthy, physically and emotionally. And eventually the animals and plant life diminished to just a few genetically modified products. Nature wasn't being hospitable to its abusive tenants. It was shutting down shop. No more would it be forced to provide sustenance for barbarians.

Orla asked Unicorn how this all could have happened. How the human race could be caught in a spiral of destruction and no one was doing anything to reverse it. He explained to his little apprentice that there had been a few people over the years who had tried to change, but they were branded cranks and charlatans. If they formed groups, they were quickly suppressed by hasty legislation. By this stage, mankind had generally stopped thinking for himself and looked to world governments to tell him what was good for him and what was dangerous. Countries had lost their sovereignty and had become part of just a few large Federations, so cultural identities and values had been lost within the large soup of so-called civilisation. The ordinary man had no idea that he was being completely manipulated. The power leaders, through the media, controlled every waking moment of their lives. It was done in a subliminal way so that the general public thought that they were making reasoned, logical decisions over their lives, but they weren't – they were all being played. Original thought had been removed from the repertoire of the masses.

Whale and Unicorn pointed out that, although the majority of people were suffering, the planet was gradually suffocating in the excess of materialism and the production and consumption of paraphernalia, the power leaders were still having a relatively luxurious life. On the backs of the suffering of the planet, they were still filling their ever-increasing coffers. 'How much gold could one person need in their life?' Orla reflected. Whale explained that the power leaders had also fallen foul to the addiction programming. The fear that fired their particular addiction was poverty. They looked around at the misery of the poor and their biggest fear was to be amongst those wretches of mankind, the disenfranchised, and so the addiction to gold seared deeply into their survival memory. Nothing was going to get in the way of filling their coffers with gold. Their lust for gold had clouded any creative thought that they might have had. That part of the brain had atrophied, the crystal memory calcified, all that was left was the instinctual primitive memory that had been inherited from their original slave-creators.

Orla observed this tableau of civilisation as it had become, and had a comedic thought which brought a smile to her otherwise disappointed demeanour: primates dressed in designer clothes were actually running the world. Orla asked Unicorn why people had not seen that their leaders were barbaric; the whole world was supposedly democratic. "Why didn't they vote for someone else?" Whale explained that there was no real choice. The programming had been so thorough that all governments had the same policies, maybe in a different format, but ultimately the message was the same. So there was no opposition, no questioning, no challenge and no real choice. Yes, people did question but not in a thorough way, fear unconsciously stopped them from doing that. This was a fear that ran so deeply in the pathways of their minds that there was no awareness that Crystal Wisdom had been compromised because that fear, no matter how scary, was very familiar and comfortable.

Whale made a decision at this point of the viewing. He knew that Orla had seen quite a lot of unpleasantness but he had to give her a better idea of how the communities had truly polarised on the planet and how they would develop in the future. On the screen Orla saw images that she did not comprehend. She looked from Whale to Unicorn for some sort of explanation but they indicated that she would understand if she kept watching. Eventually she was able to discern the confusion before her eyes and saw whole communities living under domes made of a clear glass-like substance. These were the communities of the power leaders and their many layers of helpers and aides. These communities were sheltered from the harshness of pollution and poverty and appeared to be oases of calm amongst the chaos of degeneration. Once she had absorbed this strange anomaly, she then saw the horror of where the ordinary people lived. People were living in cramped toxic societies scrabbling for the basics of water, food and shelter and were totally exposed on all levels to the evils of the physical and mental pollution, which had taken a foothold on this once beautiful planet. This polarisation was to become even more extreme when, true to form, the food supply become increasingly scarce and man needed to devise a solution to the ever decreasing ability of the Earth to support its inhabitants. But instead of looking at how the planet had become so toxic and trying to learn from his mistakes, man looked outside again, looking at his external world rather than his internal Crystal world which would have given him creative answers. The object of his gaze was another planet. Such was his simplicity, having destroyed one planet, he decided that it would be a solution to find another perfect virgin planet that demonstrated signs of life and just move on. The power leaders spent a great deal of their precious gold trying to travel to different planets using their limited man-science, desperately looking for the basic signs of life that would support them. The Crystalanders looked on from afar, watching their repeated futile attempts, desperately going from one planet to the other looking for any vital signs of life. The Crystalanders knew that, in this solar system, Earth was the only planet able to sustain these humans. All the other planets in the solar system had individual qualities, which influenced the functioning of Earth, and Earth was a collective reflection of all those qualities. The only way this solar system was going to survive was for mankind to begin to act like grown-ups and take responsibility for absolutely all of their actions.

The screen became still. Orla sat quietly for a while trying to comprehend all that she had seen. What a shock to her young system this viewing had been. She realised how lucky she was to have been born on Crystal Island and how her whole life had been so privileged. At that moment, she knew she would do anything to bring this quality of life back to the whole planet.

Orla's mentors were very pleased with their little protégé and they knew it was now time for her to go back to Crystal Island – their job was complete – but her work was just beginning. Whale bade farewell to his young student and she mounted Unicorn who led her out of the chamber, along the seabed and eventually back up again from the sea onto the beach of crystal. As they joined the turquoise crystal path Orla was deep in thought as Unicorn carried her on her final journey home. Unicorn could sense that Orla was feeling the burden of the work ahead and he interrupted her thoughts with a little trot to gain her attention and jolt her from her thoughts. She knew he had read her mind and shared her concerns about the future. He reassured her that she would be able to undertake all her responsibilities with ease but that she was not on her own. She would never become a servant to her responsibilities so that they became a burden. Her responsibilities were gifts that had been given to her only because she was able to execute them. Gifts were never bestowed unless the recipient could express them with ease. She would therefore never feel that she was carrying a heavy weight on her young shoulders. The gifts gave her direct access to all her Crystal mentors who she could call on at any time for advice by visiting the Crystal Circle on the island. But, more importantly she would have Finn; he would be at her side at all times, protecting her from anything that might overburden her on any level. He would be her equal in all matters, which gave her a wonderful sense of comfort. She had started to feel slightly isolated in her responsibilities but knowing that she could rely on her best friend and true crystal soul mate at all times dispelled all worries.

She sighed with relief and then turned her attention to

Finn. After the binding ceremony she had left the island quite quickly to start her journey to Crystaland but nearly every night of the seven years that she had been away, she had dreamed of him so it had felt as if there had been no real separation. Through her dreams she had seen how he had grown and developed over the years and had become a super-strong handsome man, which reminded her so much of her father Patrick. Patrick had once been as young and vibrant as Finn and, although he had increased in age and experience, he had lost none of his strength. His hair was still red with no signs of thinning or grey and he was still very much the strong king that he had always been. Patrick and Maeve had made a powerful couple, each complementing the other with their gifts. They too had been promised when they were fourteen and once they had completed their union, they became a very strong unit. Orla had happy memories of growing up with these two special individuals: the respect and love they demonstrated to each other was beautiful and Orla longed to experience that deep relationship with Finn.

She also could not wait to find out more about Finn's initiation into Ruby Crystaland. While she had received an initiation into that world and seen Finn for a short while, he would have spent much longer there; and, because of his male physiology, would have undergone a much more rigorous initiation. The discipline required to master his physical strength and mental ability took much practice, as his mind and body would be honed to a super human level, but he also had to learn to match that with the discernment of Wisdom. Whilst the physical and mental strengths were relatively easy to assimilate, discernment in a strong human brought many conflicting memories to the fore, which had to be transformed before a pupil could complete his initiation of the ruby Crystal world. This took a great deal of effort whereby he would have to undergo many layers of self-examination and scrutiny. The thought of meeting Finn again uplifted her mood and Unicorn picked up speed as they travelled along the crystal path.

CHAPTER FIVE

RETURN

The crystal path began to fade from its deep turquoise into the brilliant diamond crystal from her first journey leading them back to the Diamond Elders who greeted Orla with both warmth and enthusiasm. And she, not feeling a child any more, embraced them with equality. She had now the ability to read the minds of all beings of the Crystal worlds and she could sense that they were delighted with her transformation. They sat her down on a pure diamond crystal chair, which she was able to tolerate now with ease, and asked her what she had thought of planet Earth now that she had witnessed every part of its ugly degeneration.

She looked at them with a deep intensity and told them that she had seen a beautiful planet with many, many gifts, which had turned into a dustbowl teeming with people who had allowed themselves to revert from intelligent, compassionate, knowing beings into little more than primitives who had developed the intelligence of technology to the detriment of their own development into Wisdom.

They asked her if she now knew what her future responsibility would be. She did know and was not daunted by the task. The women were pleased. Had they revealed this to her before her initiation – when she was still an innocent child – she would not have understood the gravity of the responsibility required of her, nor would she have had the courage to face it, but they could see that she was now perfectly qualified for that role. She had been awakened to all the Crystal Wisdom and had not only all of its understanding, but also the qualities of protection necessary to identify and navigate the negative mindsets of the fearful, and deflect the dangers of the Shadow.

They reassured her that she would not be on her own. She and Finn would very quickly activate others on Crystal Island. The inhabitants of her island would be the first candidates as they were already programmed to a higher level than people from other lands. When she was a little older she would travel to other countries totally guarded by Finn's protection field and therefore would not be affected by the degeneration around her. Although her vibration had increased almost to the level of the Crystalanders, her human side would allow her to walk unharmed on this planet that had become, in the 22nd century, toxic on all levels. She could not be persecuted, punished or enslaved because she had awakened the ability to use her mind to outwit people who feared the change she would bring – and there would be many. She was protected from the Shadow because she had no doubt or fear to which they could attach themselves and, because of her ability to see beyond the third dimension, they would be exposed to her at all times. There was no hiding place for the Shadow from this young Crystal Warrior.

The Diamond Elders knew that in the next few years the planet would reach breaking point and Crystal Island would be asked for help. Orla's initial responsibility would be to identify people who were candidates for reawakening; people who had a certain degree of prominent Crystaland programming. She would be able to scan the world from her island and identify the few leaders who had this ability. She would approach them with her mind whilst they were sleeping which would activate in them the first stage of awakening and they would then seek her out; it was they who had to make the initial contact, as they needed to feel in total control at that stage. One by one, she would awaken a handful of people and there would only be a handful – seven in fact – which would be all it would take to turn the tides of the planet. Those leaders would ask her to identify and awaken more people who could support them and she would then bring in her team from Crystal Island who could work with them, bringing them into their full awakening.

The Elders warned that many power-people would want to be chosen as candidates and would try to mould themselves into the necessary selection criteria – the human quick fix idea – as they would perceive this as another opportunity to flex their power muscle. However, there was one clear way of detecting whether an individual was a true candidate. It was to be found in their voice: the tone of a person's voice could not be manipulated. If they had prominent Crystal memory then they had their own personal song encrypted into their words and Crystal knowledge allowed the initiated to see the colour and form of the sound that people produced when they spoke. The tone of an individual who had less fear was very different from that of someone with dominant primitive programming. Once those authentic candidates had been identified and reprogrammed, the Shadow attachments would shrivel and retreat and eventually be forced to leave Earth. This would be the dawn of the rebirth. The Earth was dying and it had requested one more chance to be reborn – the future of the planet and its solar system was dependent on the awakening of just a handful of people… but, as always, just a few pure crystals is all it takes to begin a new process of transformation.

And so Orla bade farewell to the Diamond Elders and walked back along the white diamond crystal path with her faithful unicorn to where her travelling vessel had been waiting for the past years. Such was her transformation that it was not necessary to go through the energy portal to return home; she was now able to travel seamlessly between the different levels of Earth and the various Crystal worlds. Unicorn silently reflected on this special girl's future. He knew she had been successfully prepared to undertake all her responsibilities but he knew that she had many challenges to face. She would face such opposition from the power leaders on one hand and then the Shadow would gather all their hatred and direct it towards her. They would ramp up the hatred dial in their hosts bodies and would then use every opportunity to outwit, tempt, bribe and generally distract her, and the people close to her, from her path. He knew that she would be successful but it would be a challenging journey. He wished he could have gone with her to make her journey just a little easier but it was impossible, he knew that he would never have survived on Earth. He also knew that at times she would be nearly emotionally depleted by the work that she had to do even with the forceful protection of Finn, and it was at those times that she would need to return to Crystaland. Orla turned to Unicorn and hugged his neck tightly not wanting to let go. She wanted to show her appreciation for all that he had been to her over these years – she had been gone from home for seven Earth years. He had been her friend, her guide, her mentor and most of all her trusted companion.

Unicorn reassured her that she now had free access to the travelling vessel and she could come back to Crystaland at any time. She could move freely between the two realms without creating damage to her physical body. She was both reassured and delighted as the fascination of the Crystal worlds would always be a strong attraction for her. He told her that she would also need to come back at various times in her life to recalibrate her crystal side and, not wanting to give her any indication of the dangers of the roads she would travel, whenever she returned he would always be there waiting for her to accompany her.

She moved towards the open door of the travelling sphere and waved goodbye as the door closed. She sat down on the crystal seat and miraculously was able to enter the correct code on the dimpled panel. In anticipation of her return to Earth, she removed her golden slippers and put on her normal day shoes. She sat back, closed her eyes and allowed her thoughts to run unhindered through her mind. Within minutes she had landed and the door of the vessel opened. She was home and felt an overwhelming sense of delayed homesickness, a feeling that had not occurred in all the time that she had been away as she had been preoccupied with so much information that had suffused every cell of her body and mind. Now that she was back, she began to realise all that she had missed and wondered if life would be different now that she had completed her initiation. She stepped out of the vessel and walked apprehensively through the opening of the tree. She was back again in the Secret Garden. She initially thought that nothing would have changed, but as soon as she stepped into the garden, within a split second she was overwhelmed by sounds. The cacophony in her head forced her to put her hands to her ears and squeeze her eyes shut as her eyes were also playing tricks on her and her head began to swim with what she was seeing.

She gradually opened her eyes, took a deep breath in, exhaled and, finding herself more balanced, observed her environment. She was amazed at what she was seeing. The gardeners were working away as always; the plants and flowers were growing happily but she could see the communication between the plants and the gardeners; she was able to see the 'sounds' that they were making to each other by reading the ripples passing through the space between them which changed colour with the changing of the octaves. She gradually removed her hands from her ears, one at a time, and was able to identify the many sounds that were coming from everything around her and the colours that were coming from the sounds. It was as if each plant had its own signature tune and gradually she was able to make sense of the jumbled onslaught on all her senses, and was able to discern and focus on each plant individually. Each plant gave her information about its qualities and the space that it occupied in the garden. She knelt down and gently stroked the delicate petal of a rose and immediately felt the tingling of information pass into her fingers from the whole rose bush.

Her senses had been blown wide open on Crystaland giving her the ability to read everything in her environment visible and invisible to the uninitiated eye. This was a skill that would be vital to her later when she had to identify people in positions of authority in the world who were suitable for the Crystaland transformation process. She gazed over at the grove of trees and they smiled to her in approval, she was now aware of the qualities of each tree that her grandmother had originally explained to her and, to her amazement, she was able to communicate with them as an equal. The trees nodded their welcome with their branches as she walked along the grove touching each tree in turn feeling the information from the trees pass through her body via all her senses. She stood still, soaking in the feeling of being in communion with all the plants, trees and the gardeners. It was an intoxicating and glorious feeling making her deeply thankful and grateful for that privilege.

Her mother was eagerly waiting for her in the garden. She had sensed when Orla would be returning and had made her way to the garden full of excitement as she had missed her beloved daughter but, more importantly, she was excited to discover how she had matured. The two women greeted each other with a huge embrace and Maeve observed all the changes in her daughter. Yes, she was seven year older and she had matured on many levels, but her physiology had made several shifts of change. Her skin and eyes had the telltale luminosity of Crystaland, which her mother identified immediately, together with the strands of white speckled through her hair. After each princess had returned from Crystaland, they all had the same look about them; it was as if light bounced off their skin radiating back into the environment. But, most of all Maeve observed her child's Crystal maturity. This was not just the maturity that seven years would have given; this was the inner majesty that she projected from every cell of her body which took Maeve's breath away with pride. She knew that within that majesty was the most important understanding of the humility of responsibility and Orla wore that mantle with ease.

The two women linked arms and walked back through the Secret Garden to the palace in silence. There was no need for words. Both knew exactly what had transpired and what would happen next. Thus it was for the women of the Crystaland royal bloodline.

Orla stop speaking and looked down at her sleeping children, her gaze drinking in every detail of their faces that were reflecting the changes brought about by adolescence. She knew that this was as far as she could go with the story. She would have to wait until they were a few years older before she could embark on Part Two. In the quietness of the room she reflected on the years between her returning from Crystaland and the rollercoaster of events that followed, where the Earth was grabbed from the jaws of a dystopian future to the privileged place it now occupied. Her role and that of Finn's was pivotal to the planet's transformation and their reward had been their twins. She looked down at them with a deep tenderness and love, a love that sometimes overwhelmed her, but she knew that they too had an important destiny, they too carried the bloodline of the royal family, and they, like her, had a responsibility to perpetuate Crystal Wisdom. She also knew that this was probably the biggest challenge yet to be placed at the feet of royal children. As a mother, she wanted to totally protect them but, as a princess, she knew that they had a responsibility and duty to fulfill. They both had unique gifts and abilities, and the entire future of all the universes would eventually rest firmly and confidently on their shoulders.

About the Author

Colleen O'Flaherty-Hilder has been a Health and Wellness Practitioner for over 35 years. Her initial training in Mind Dynamics in 1981 prompted her interest, which became a passion, into how emotions affect physical health. After extensive research, trainings and personal experience she created Alchemical Transformation Programmes™ that embraces a confluence of modalities to facilitate profound change on the physical, mental, emotional and spiritual levels.

www.colleenoflaherty.co.uk